FOREWORDS

This lovely and poetic book is the work of a very old friend, who is very Chinese and thus difficult to define or classify in Western terms. Obviously he is a poet and an artist. He is also a scholar, but not in our sense—not such a pedantic sinologist who would be recognized, for example, by the American Oriental Society. Gia-fu Feng is not writing *about* the old Chinese way of life: he represents it; he *is* it; and is, therefore, the actual substance which our scholars study, "about it and about." He shows us the Tai Chi exercises and the feeling of the I Ching, or Book of Changes, from a basic, grass-roots, point of view.

This will not, I think, offend Gia-fu. He is a marvelous example of the Chinese ideal of the old rogue—the wandering, impecunious, poetic, and mildly disreputable type of Taoist sage embodying the principle of the Tao (or Course of Nature), "which forces nothing and yet leaves nothing undone."

Zen Buddhist monks are known as cloud-water people, because they drift like clouds and flow like water. This is Gia-fu, who, believe it or not, was at one time a banker in China, but who is now a most creative dropout in the mountains of Big Sur and Los Gatos in California.

I recommend this book most warmly.
Alan Watts

There are two universes in which we have our being—one on each side of our skin. In what proportion are we aware of these two immensities and under which circumstances? It is generally in the act of love that most of us are especially aware of what goes on simultaneously in both universes, and, when all is well, of their dissolving boundaries and emergence into one. There are also other ways to experience and enjoy our inner and outer worlds and their unification: one of the most subtle esthetic and generally beneficial ways is Tai Chi Chuan. I would think that it is the variety of enjoyment given by Tai Chi Chuan that holds its centuries-long fascination.

For the person dedicated to physical discipline and endurance Tai Chi Chuan represents a training of the highest order: the slowness and precision of the movements develop physical skill and endurance; to know the sequence of the one hundred and eight forms is an achievement of perseverance and memory.

For the person interested in intellectual speculation, symbols, philosophy, and history Tai Chi Chuan offers a challenge: for what is *really* the meaning of the forms called "White Stork Flapping Its Wings," or "Jade Girl Threading at the Shuttle," or "Repulsing the Monkey," or "Needle at the Bottom of the Sea"?

For those who enjoy expression through the body, imagine the fun of transforming those words into aneverchangingneverstoppingalwaysroundlyflowing motion!

Imagine the pleasure of feeling, as you slowly "Waving Hands Like Clouds," the shifting of weight, the change of pressure and temperature inside of you, the giving and taking of muscles, of experiencing those inseparable forces of Yin and Yang.

For the masculine type Tai Chi Chuan is the training of the warrior—the expression is impassable, powerful, hard: he is the winner, every time.

But for the feminine type there is hardly any activity more graceful, smooth, soothing—even tender.

And the esthete? His is possibly the greatest pleasure—for, while perfecting his body-mind, he has the privilege of tracing forms of evanescent beauty—freer than a sculptor who works with solid matter, he is modeling a yielding element of life—the air—with the highest instrument of life—the body-mind.

Tai Chi Chuan is generally performed in silence—or Silence. In either case the musician can innerly listen to the music he chooses for his own version of Tai Chi Chuan.

As Tai Chi Chuan becomes part of Western culture it will probably develop in many different ways, as it will have a different meaning for each individual or group. Generally, however, it produces a union of inner and outer, of body and soul, of contemplation and action—all of this on the nonverbal level! Therefore no more words from me—let us experience Tai Chi Chuan rather than dissect it.

Laura A. Huxley

I Ching—A Guide to Oracle Imagery and Tai Chi—A Way of Centering

---

My chief concern is how to be in tune with the Tao 道, the ever-changing cosmic rhythm. But what is the Tao 道? The I Ching, or Book of Changes, enumerates sixty-four major possible happenings.

The translation of the sixty-four hexagrams presented in this book is from the Ch'ien-lung edition published in the late eighteenth century. Professor Jerome Kirk of the Program in Language and Development at the University of California, Irvine, collaborated in the translation, which may be regarded as a prelude to our more complete and scholarly translation and manual for the I Ching. Our effort, in the rendering presented here, was to be as perfectly straightforward as possible, while using the full range of expression available in contemporary American English. Heng 亨, for example, usually translated "progress," or "success," has virtually the same range of connotation of joyous enthusiasm and unerring direction as does the colloquial term "groovy," and we have translated it accordingly. Fu 孚, generally translated "truthfulness," or "sincerity," is an almost magical virtue in a leader which leads people to follow him in blind faith; we use the word "charisma."

The Chinese classics always fascinate me. In doing this translation I relived the days in my teens when, during summer vacations, I was put under strict discipline by traditional masters in a family country villa near Shanghai. That was before the Japanese invasion of 1937, which put an end to the classical Chinese culture. From the ages of nine to seventeen I was sent to a boarding school, something like a monastery. I was allowed to go home only one day a month. In this school I was taught various subjects in the traditional way, including Tai Chi Chuan.

Tai Chi Chuan is a form of meditation in movement. It is a way of centering, aiming at sensomotoric awareness and body alignment. It corrects the posture and enhances relaxation. It energizes the body and tranquilizes the spirit. It is a bridge between Eastern meditation and Western psychotherapy, integrating the mind and the senses.

Tao 道 Heng 亨 Fu 孚

Gia-fu Feng

PREFATORY NOTE

The material in this book had its origins at a time when the forebears of the Athenian Greeks were half-civilized Ionian nomads. Yet it is a peculiarly modern, as well as peculiarly sophisticated, book.

In Western, and particularly in American, culture, the Protestant religions (along with protestantized Catholicism, Judaism, and Communism) have emphasized the values of prediction and control. It has seemed more virtuous to make predictable profits by the efficient use of rational accounting than simply to get rich. In the development of the United States, it has been almost a religious necessity to maintain a good credit rating without spending money on anything pleasurable. The social systems generated by centuries when these values predominated tend to become efficient, democratic, and affluent.

For some time, however, a new kind of objection has been raised to this outcome—not by reactionaries who long to return to feudalism, but by some of those most firmly committed to the pragmatic, libertarian, rationalistic values underlying our cultures. David Riesman, in the fifties, observed the development of the "other-directed" character, while William H. Whyte Jr. saw the sprouting of a "social ethic" to replace the "Protestant ethic." Now, psychotherapy is inundated with a sequence of "revolutions," and there are amateur encounter groups on virtually every college campus and in many large corporations. Organized religion seems on the verge of being ripped apart by internal schisms. Academics, psychedelic hedonists, and the leisure classes cast about for new ways of knowing. A new "head music" generates ecstatic rituals among children and young adults, whose parents can only hold their ears and wince from the volume. In 1968, a handful of these same young people frivoled for a few days in Lincoln Park and shook the bureaucratic foundations of the Democratic party and the City of Chicago.

It is hardly an accident that in these decades so many of the trappings of non-Western religions enjoy popularity. The functions served so well by Protestant-type religions no longer seem essential to a large segment of the population. Yet, needs are felt that are not satisfied by the secular Protestantism which passes for agnostic objectivity.

Tai Chi and the Roots of Chinese Religion

The oldest religion (or class of religions) in China has no name, though it was around for many centuries before Buddha, Confucius, or Lao-tzŭ and strongly influenced the thought of the latter two. I call it Sinism. Sinism was a religion of ancestor spirits and household gods, with a pantheon which varied considerably from one part of China to another. Notable in this pantheon were the pioneer emperors, said to have lived about 5,000 years ago: Fu Hsi, the inventor of civilization and writing; Shen Nung, the inventor of agriculture; and Huang Ti, the inventor of government and medicine. By no means, however, was Sinism a mere primitive animism. Rather it contained an elaborate cosmology, morality, and social philosophy.

Philosophically, Sinism is based on Tai Chi, the ultimate unity, with its two faces of Yin (dark softness) and Yang (light toughness). Tai Chi is represented by the well-known circle divided into two complementary teardrops, one light and the other dark. In the center of the light teardrop is a point of dark Yin; in the center of the dark one is a point of light Yang. Yang and Yin represent among other things good and bad, male and female, firm and yielding, day and night, south and north, heaven and earth, odd and even, and all the other simple dichotomies equally comprehensible to the Western mind. Tai Chi represents their relationship. This relationship is not one of polar opposition but one of unity. Many Western clichés express similar ideas: "Everything is relative—there can be no south without north, or maleness without femaleness"; "Beyond good and evil"; "Compassion is strength; belligerence is weakness." Western mathematics, too, toys with this idea. Plus and minus are oddly symmetrical, and the world can perhaps equally well be represented by changing all the signs in a mathematical model. (Some of the ramifications of this idea constitute the hottest issues in the physics of the last decade.) The binary system of numeration (which could just as well be notated by solid and broken horizontal lines as by the circles and vertical lines we use for zero and one) is convenient not only for computers but for many of the general propositions of modern algebra. Examples could be multiplied indefinitely.

It does not seem unreasonable, as a matter of fact, to treat the Tai Chi as a kind of mathematical model of the universe. It is a fruitful conventional representation of reality, as are the equations of physics and chemistry. Reality cannot of course be captured on paper, as Lao-tzŭ says in the first sentence of his book; but that is not the point. The difference between Oriental and Western models of the world is one of pragmatism. To the Chinese, the ability of Caucasians (including East Indians) to get hung up in metaphysical abstractions is a never-ending source of wonder. Our mathematics is said to have begun with Euclid's idea of the triangle. Not any particular triangle, mind you, but the abstract essence of triangularity. The fact that the Western mind is chained by its capacity to dwell on such things often confuses the Chinese (although the introduction of Buddhist and Marxist thought into China has done a great deal to bring convergence). After all, Tai Chi represents a unique thing in the real world; and the Sinist would never confuse the representation with reality, for he would never have the occasion to discuss any reality that grandly general. When he talks about reality, he talks about real, fist-bangable-against manifestations.

The organizing principle of Tai Chi served very much the same function in Chinese culture and science as has mathematics in Western science since the Renaissance. The Chinese have felt that Tai Chi was a logical principle; consequently, it is of equal applicability in modeling physical phenomena, social phenomena, and biological phenomena. It captures the valid analogies between calendar cycles and human history, among cognitive organization, interpersonal relationships, and institutional structure, and so on. From this idea come notions which may be regarded as religious, but alternatively may be regarded as the theory and technique of a positive social science. The idea of Wei wu wei (doing without bothering) is a manifestation of strength through yielding and vice versa. The circular quality of Tai Chi is a felicitous notation which continually reminds us of many things: the brittleness of straight lines, the cyclic quality of so many natural and social phenomena, the importance of boundaries. Leibnitz was most impressed, upon encountering the Tai Chi, to discover in it a number of mathematical inventions he had regarded as his own—not only the binary system, but also the calculus of change.

The Branches of Sinism

We are often told that there are three main religions in Chinese history: Buddhism, Confucianism, and Taoism. Actually, there are many more than three religions, but all have in common the Sinist basis; to Western eyes they are similar to one another.

Confucius (styled Chung-ni) was born into the Sinist tradition and adopted the larger part of it as a basis for his own teaching. He was a formalizer. Today we would probably regard him as rather an authoritarian sort. He would probably be a political sociologist working for the Rand Corporation, hoping continually to be appointed presidential advisor in one administration after another. Confucius was particularly sensitive to the ways in which the properties of social interaction lubricate history. He urged that people obey social conventions, not out of any pious conformity but because they are finely tuned instruments for getting things done efficiently. He must be regarded as one of the world's greatest administrative theorists. In his later years, Confucius turned to the first Sinist classic, the I Ching. Most of the commentaries in modern editions of the book were written by Confucius and his followers, and although it was an ancient document when Confucius first encountered it, I Ching is traditionally awarded the status of a "Confucian" classic. Confucius was more of a mystic than a mystifier, so he had very little patience with spiritualistic mumbo-jumbo. He simply refused to discuss some topics—including most of those a Westerner would recognize as religious—on the same grounds as would a modern physicist or psychologist, speaking professionally. Because of this Confucianist distaste for obscurity and ornamentation, Confucianism has lacked the romantic appeal of Zen Buddhism or Hinduism to unconventional Westerners. By the same token, however, Confucian-Sinist styles of thought are quite acceptable to the agnostic Western scientist or man of affairs.

Lao-tzŭ (if the man existed) may actually have been considerably senior to Confucius, but his philosophy (as stated in the Tao Te Ching and by his followers, notably Chüan-tzŭ and Lieh-tzu) may best be understood as a response to

Confucianism. Lao-tzŭ accused Confucius of being an establishment stuffed shirt and of having the kind of excessive conformity typical of the not quite successful, striving professional man. He also felt that Confucius underestimated the effectiveness of Yin forces, explicitly recommended dropping out of public life, and was thought of as rather a hippie by Confucianists. Lao-tzŭ believed in nonviolence as a tactic. Many military men, turning Taoist at the end of their careers, chafed nevertheless at the extreme contemplative quietude of the Shao-lin and other monasteries. One of the outcomes of this arrangement was the creation of meditation disciplines based on the highest martial arts of the day. (Mendicant Taoist monks traveling along the bandit-ridden roads of China also found it convenient while being attacked to be able to practice their meditation disciplines in such a way that the clumsy bandits injured themselves.) This is another fundamental source of Tai Chi Chuan. A related achievement of Taoism was the development of Chinese medicine. This set of techniques, ranging from dietary rules to acupuncture and mocsibustion, is based largely on theories of the Five Elements. This is another ramification of the basic theory of Tai Chi and was a highly significant influence on later analyses of the I Ching. This and other early Sinist notions are nonsense by the standards of contemporary Western biology. The Chinese disinclination to surgical therapeutics was so extreme that the anatomy postulated by the Chinese medical tradition seems contradicted by the simplest autopsy. Nevertheless, that tradition involves a wide variety of curative techniques of undisputed effectiveness and is given equal emphasis with Western medicine in the medical schools of the (equally pragmatic, but Western-oriented) Communist regime today.

Meanwhile, in India, Buddhism was being developed, partly as an extension of, partly a revolt against Hinduism. Exported to China, it was almost immediately seized upon by Sinists and Taoists and turned into the typically Chinese Ch'an (Japanese: Zen) Buddhism. The metaphysical and psychological elements in Chinese philosophy are thus of foreign origin.

In the last century or so another foreign influence—Western philosophy and technology, specifically in Marxist Communism—has entered the Chinese tradition, and it appears that the same transformation is being performed upon it.

Interestingly, twentieth-century Western thought (notably in the physical sciences) has been adopted straightforwardly and with little difficulty. The Chinese train nuclear physicists as well as anyone else. Nineteenth-century Western (particularly German) thought, on the other hand, has proven uniquely difficult for Chinese to deal with. Thus, Chinese Communism is continually tortured by the necessity of reconciling the wisdom of Karl Marx to the pragmatic Chinese nature, and Chinese Communism is like no Western version of that religion.

The Two Rituals of Tai Chi

This book provides instructions for performing two related though different religious ceremonies. The primary appeal of these ceremonies, paradoxically, is to the hard-minded, rather than to the delicate; to the lusty, rather than to the pious.

Some thousands of years before Christ, the Sinist tradition developed an oracle from the premise of the Tai Chi. According to legend, Fu Hsi, the first emperor, observed that Yin and Yang may each be divided (or combined, if you will, since it is the same thing to a Sinist) into great or old, and young or small. Great Yang, ⚌, for example, has such an excess of Yang that it is on the way to becoming Yin. Small Yang, ⚍, is less drastically Yang and so more stable. This identification of opposites, $+\infty = -\infty$, is a central feature of the Tai Chi philosophy. (It, too, occurs in Western mathematics, in the context of projective geometry.)

Fu Hsi is also said to have proposed the further division/combination of these elements into threefold permutations (kua), which we call trigrams. Thus, Old Yang generates Ch'ien ☰ (Heaven, meaning strength) and Tui ☱ (pleasure, meaning shallow water). Young Yang yields Li ☲ (beauty, meaning flame) and Chen ☳ (shaking, meaning thunder). Old Yin gives rise to K'un ☷ (Earth, meaning submission) and Ken ☶ (stopping, meaning mountain). Young Yin begets K'an ☵ (hole, meaning deep water) and Sun ☴ (mild, meaning wind and wood). To introduce our translation of the I Ching, we selected from the ten appendices the eighth wing, Shuo Kua, the essay on these Pa Kua (eight trigrams).

The essences of these trigrams are embodied in an intricate circular sequence of body movements called Pa Kua (or, more phonetically, particularly in South China, Bok Qua). These traditional movements manifest various philosophical tenets of Sinism: the instant alternation of empty yielding (Yin) with solid force (Yang); the compass points North (K'un), East (K'an), South (Ch'ien) and West (Li); the relationship of movement (Chen) and stability (Ken) with impulse (Tui) and restraint (Sun). The I Ching describes the social-philosophical implications, while the Tai Chi Chuan (fist) represents the body movements of the sixty-four permutations of these eight trigrams.

Tai Chi Chuan as such is no more than a thousand years old, and the version presented in this book comes in the last decade from the Ministry of Physical Education of the People's Republic of China. The I Ching of this volume, however, comes from King Wen and his son Tan (the Duke of Chou) who lived a bit before 1000 B.C. The sixty-four sixfold permutations of the Pa Kua (called hexagrams in English to distinguish them from the threefold kua) are said (along with Tan's sixty-four variations on each) to model all the possible social situations in which the Superior Man might find himself. King Wen organized these situations in the I Ching, the Book of Changes or "Easy Handbook," in order to release the wise administrator from dependence on unstable priestly types for interpreting the oracle. The Duke of Chou perfected the handbook by exploring the meaning of the various lines of the hexagrams. Since that time many eminent Chinese theologians and social scientists have written commentaries and glosses for the modern I Ching, which is thus a compendium of observations by the wisest Chinese of three millenia. The I Ching is a handbook of administration, an object of religious devotion, an analysis of subconscious imagery, a cosmological treatise, a weather forecast, and a guide to mental health. Tai Chi Chuan is a dramatic answer to skeptical questions about Oriental religion. It is a set of principles of self-defense, a hobby, an orthopedic instrument, a means of meditation, a prophylaxis against disease, a philosophical system, and a beautiful dance. These movements, while difficult to master, can be approximated even by the Westerner in a relatively few hours of study and practice. The results of performing them—even of performing them badly—are amazing. The student discovers that he feels more refreshed and energetic after doing the exercise than he did when he started. The euphoric feeling of the movements "doing themselves" makes the concept of wei wu wei comprehensible. Almost immediately, his postural alignment and balance are improved; in a few weeks, this easy and pleasurable exercise makes visible changes in his body.

Why a New Version?

It seems to me rather unfortunate that so many of the brilliant men who have labored to open East Asian thought to Western eyes have been to such an extent creatures of the unusually non-Chinese nineteenth-century culture: Karlfried Duerckheim, Eugen Herrigel, James Legge, Carl Jung, Richard Wilhelm, and others. In the best *Stürm und Drang* tradition of Germanic romanticism many of these men have repeatedly fallen into an ideological need to display how effective is the Chinese use of sensitive and esoteric wisdom intrinsically incomprehensible to English shopkeepers and American cowboys. The point is, of course, that Chinese wisdom is a meat-and-potatoes kind of wisdom. It is humble, plain, and practical. It is far more easily comprehensible to the simple cowboy (or the engineer) than to the grand, ornate, crepuscular, and compulsively manly Aryan mind. Probably most of the pioneer Sinologists ended their lives in mental institutions.

To Chao-shu ("summon the books") as Gia-fu Feng was called in China, Chinese and American cultures show great similarity. I know of no one else who underwent the classical Chinese education before I was born and who is also so fluent in the language and culture of Americans. Like the prototypical Sinist scholar, Chao-shu calls himself a Buddhist, Confucianist, and Taoist. Apparently like many hip Western students of similar circumstances he had the means and desire to travel widely around his continent, studying foreign scholarship —what we call Oriental religion. He even came to America to study our exotic Protestant religion, a study which involved him in being a Wall Street banker for a while and in doing advanced graduate study in business administration and the social sciences at American universities. In many ways, however, he feels that the rhetoric of young people now is more Chinese even than the rhetoric of administration. Thus, his I Ching says things to us like, "that's groovy!"

Here, then, is the message of the Tai Chi. The calligraphy, the bodies in motion, and the poetry of the Easy Handbook have the same message. Look at the Tao.

J. Kirk
Laguna Beach
May, 1969

I CHING

A Book of Oracle Imagery, in a New Translation
by Gia-fu Feng
and Jerome Kirk

EDITOR'S NOTE

The I Ching (or Book of Changes) forms the ground of philosophical and religious thought and practice out of which Tai Chi comes to flower. The reader will find the first part of this book, an introduction to the I Ching, quite easy to understand if he simply follows the sequence of parts set by the authors. This discussion is divided into the following parts:

I. The "Eighth Wing," an essay on the trigrams (elements) explaining the ancient origins of the eight trigrams involved in forming the oracle-imagery known as I Ching.

II. Notes on various ways to cast the oracle, with an explanation of some of the key terms and concepts involved.

III. The I Ching: The sixty-four hexagrams.

I
The "Eighth Wing"
THE ESSAY ON THE TRIGRAMS (Shuo Kua)

1. The holy sages composed the I in ancient times.

In solitary silence with God's light, they created the yarrow stalks.

They assigned 3 to heaven and 2 to earth;

From these they derived the other numbers.[1]

They studied the changes of Yin and Yang, and established the hexagrams.

From the enhanced movement of the tough and the soft they produced the individual lines.

They yielded to the harmony of Tao and Te and accurately computed the proper relationships.[2]

Through this exhaustive rationale, covering all of nature, they arrived at destiny.

2. The holy sages composed the I in ancient times.

They deliberately surrendered to the principles of their natures and of destiny.

They established the Tao of heaven to be Yin and Yang;

They established the Tao of earth to be toughness and softness;

They established the Tao of man to be humanness and loyalty.

They combined these three virtues and doubled them, so the I contains hexagrams.

The Yin and Yang places are differentiated and alternately occupied by the tough and the soft.[3]

This accomplished the diagrams.

3. Heaven and earth are set in position;

Mountain and lake interact;

Thunder and wind provoke each other;

Water and fire coexist;

The eight trigrams commingle.

Counting the past is forward.

Knowing the future is backward.

Thus, the I is counting backward.[4]

4. Thunder moves things;

Wind scatters them.

Rain moistens things.

The Sun dries them.

K'an stops things;

Tui pleases them.

Ch'ien rules things;

K'un preserves them.

5. God comes from Chen (shock, thunderous movement); Things are brought to completion by Sun (gentle penetration); they see each other as though by Li (beautiful clinging flame); they serve one another like K'un; they follow their own desires like Tui (shallow lake, pleasure); they provoke things like Ch'ien; they work like K'an (deep water, dangerous pit); they rest like Ken stillness, mountain).

The ten thousand things originate in Chen in the east.[5]

They are structured through Sun in the southeast. (This structure is the cleanness of the ten thousand things.)

Li is the light by which they see each other, the trigram of the south. (The holy sages faced south to listen to the ten thousand things; then they administered them well. They took that practice from this trigram.)

K'un means the earth, which nourishes the ten thousand things. (Thus it is said, "They serve each other in K'un.")

Tui is mid-autumn, when ten thousand things rejoice. (Thus it is said, "They follow their own desires like Tui.")

They fight in Ch'ien, the trigram of the northwest. (Here, the Yin and Yang provoke each other.)

K'an is water, the trigram of due north, where the ten thousand things return. (Thus it is said, "They work like K'an.")

Ken is the northeastern trigram, and in it is the beginning and end of the ten thousand things. (Thus it is said, "They rest like Ken.")

6. The spirit is unfathomably manifest in ten thousand things.

For moving things, nothing is faster than thunder.

For swaying things, nothing is faster than the wind.

For parching things, there is nothing hotter than fire.

For gladdening things, there is nothing more pleasing than the lake.

For moistening things, there is nothing wetter than water.

For beginning and ending things, there is nothing more lush than the mountain.

Therefore, water and fire corporate, thunder and wind do not interfere with each other, mountain and lake mute their spirits.

In this way, they can make the ten thousand things change, grow, and fulfill themselves.

quick-triple-your-money. It is the impatient trigram.

K'an is water, ditch bog hidden lurking straighten-bent bow wheel. As to man,

☰	☷	☳	☴	☵	☲	☶	☱
乾	坤	震	巽	坎	離	艮	兌
Ch'ien	K'un	Chen	Sun	K'an	Li	Ken	Tui
Strength	Accept-ing	Shaking	Gentle	Abysmal	Clinging	Stillness	Pleasure
Heaven	Earth	Thunder	Wind	Water	Flame	Moun-tain	Lake
7. healthy	easy	moving	penetrat-ing	trapping	beautiful	stopping	happy
8. horse	cow	dragon	rooster	hawk	pheasant	dog	sheep
9. head	belly	foot	thigh	ear	eye	hand	mouth
10. father	mother	oldest son	oldest daughter	middle son	middle daughter	young-est son	youngest daughter

11. Ch'ien is Heaven round king father jade gold cold ice great red. As to horses, good old wiry fierce. It is a fruit-bearing tree.

K'un is earth mother cloth pot stinginess boy-mother-cow large-carriage flowering populace handle impartiality based. As to soils, it is black.

Chen is thunder dragon ochre spreading freeway first-boy decisive impatient young-bamboo reed-rush; as to horses, good-whinnier left-hindleg prancing white-tuft-forehead. As to cultivated plants, returning from seed in the end strong fresh prospering.

Sun is wood wind first-daughter plumb-line labor white long high advance-and-retreat indecisive stink. As to people, bald wide-forehead white-eye get-rich-

anxiety insanity earache; it is the trigram of blood ruddy. As to horses, beautiful-back high-spirit hanging-head thin-hoof dragging-step. As to vehicle, it is a lemon. It is coming-through moon thief. As to trees, hard full-hearted.

Li is fire sun electricity middle-daughter armor helmet lance sword. As to men, phony. It is the trigram of creativity turtle crab snail mussel tortoise. As to trees, hollow and dried out above.

Ken is mountain trail pebble gateway fruits temple-cop finger seeds dog rat strong-beaked. As to trees, strong knotty.

Tui is shallow marshy pool youngest-daughter witch mouth tongue picking smashing attachment. As to soils, strong salty. It is a concubine bitchy sheep.

II
Notes on Casting and Terms

[1] There are two ways of casting the oracle in common use both in Asia and in the West. The coin oracle is quicker and simpler (a feature not universally considered an advantage since it discourages serious contemplation and reverence), but it distorts the "lines." The stick oracle is the oldest method.

Both techniques involve selecting a ritual number 6, 7, 8, or 9 for each of the six lines of the hexagram beginning at the bottom. Odd numbers (7 and 9) are Yang lines, and even numbers (6 and 8) are Yin lines;

6 ——X—— Old (moving) Yin
7 ———— Young Yang
8 —— —— Young Yin
9 ——o—— Old (moving) Yang.

Whenever an "old" line is cast, the elaboration or modification of the oracle associated with that position (beginning, 2, 3, 4, 5, or top) becomes relevant. Furthermore, the hexagram obtained changes to a second hexagram indicating the tendency or outcome of the situation.

For example, suppose the sequence 6–7–9–7–8–8 is cast:

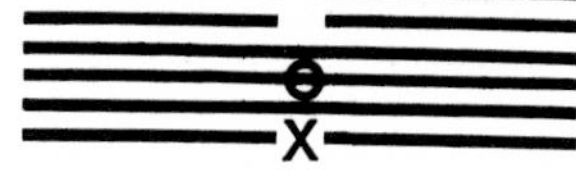

The oracle obtained is No. 32, THE CONSTANT, with lines 1 (beginning) and 3. We read:

THE CONSTANT is groovy.
He is not at fault.
Steadiness is profitable.
Going somewhere is profitable.
Not constantly following virtue is shameful. Steadiness brings regret.
Deep constancy. Steadiness brings disaster. Nothing is profitable.

An auspicious hexagram, but modified in an ominous direction by the lines, which specifically contradict the third sentence of the text. The tendency or outcome of this situation is illustrated by the hexagram obtained by letting each old line move to its contrary:

[1] Shnoka, I. 4, p. 8.

This is No. 54, MARRYING OFF LITTLE SISTER. This text reads:
Marrying off little sister.
Aggressiveness brings disaster.
It is unprofitable.

The following table is useful for identifying the hexagrams so obtained, until such familiarity is gained that it becomes unnecessary.

UPPER TRIGRAM

LOWER TRIGRAM	Heaven	Lake	Flame	Thunder	Wind	Water	Mountain	Earth
Heaven	1	43	14	34	9	5	26	11
Lake	10	58	38	54	61	60	41	19
Flame	13	49	30	55	37	63	22	36
Thunder	25	17	21	51	42	3	27	24
Wind	44	28	50	32	57	48	18	46
Water	6	47	64	40	59	29	4	7
Mountain	33	31	56	62	53	39	52	15
Earth	12	45	35	16	20	8	23	2

The Coin Oracle

This oracle uses three identical coins (although one could be flipped three times instead). It is necessary to decide which side of the coin is Yin and which is Yang. For some reason, most people select tails to be the Yang side, so that will be assumed here. The three coins are tossed. Since even is Yin and odd is Yang, we assign the number 2 (the smallest even number) to heads and the number 3 (the smallest odd number) to tails. Adding up the numbers from the three coins, we have four possibilities:

3 heads $2 + 2 + 2 = 6$ —X— Old Yin
2 heads $2 + 2 + 3 = 7$ ——— Young Yang
2 tails $2 + 3 + 3 = 8$ — — Young Yin
3 tails $3 + 3 + 3 = 9$ —o— Old Yang

Even more frivolous than the coin oracle is the license-plate oracle. This device was invented in California for use while driving down freeways. California license plates contain a group of three digits. If all odd numbers are assigned the odd number 3, while all even numbers (including 0) are assigned the even number 2, each automobile selected will represent a single line, and any six cars determine a hexagram with its associated lines. Many feel that this means of determining the oracle is impious and can cause the oracle to degenerate to a sort of parlor game. It is hardly more so than the coin device, however. The difficulty with both is that oracles cast in these ways often prove difficult to interpret since the caster is rarely in a very sensitive, contemplative mood. One strong virtue of the license-plate oracle is that, to be used by the driver (who cannot pause to look anything up), it entails sufficient study of the hexagrams that, either by memorizing them or by contemplating their structure, the oracle obtained can be recognized for what it is.

The Stick Oracle

Traditionally, stalks of yarrow fifteen to twenty inches long are used for this oracle. Although some attribute mystical properties to the plant, yarrow was selected because it used to grow wild in the back country where the oracle was cast. Pick-up sticks, chopsticks, or anything else which may be held between the fingers will do.

For each line using the stick oracle, forty-nine sticks are sorted three times (as though one were throwing a coin three times). Each sort provides either a 2 or a 3, so the sum total is 6, 7, 8, or 9 just as with the coin oracle. (The statistical difference is that in the coin oracle a Yin line is just as apt to be moving as a Yang line. With the sticks, the Yang lines are three times as likely to be "old" as the Yin lines.)

A set of fifty sticks is used. They are counted off by fours until only two are left. One of these two is set aside and not used again. The remaining forty-nine are shaken in a container and divided into two groups of roughly equal size. These two groups will be called the right-hand and left-hand groups. One stick is taken from the right-hand group and placed between the third and fourth fingers of the left hand. While holding it, the left-hand group is picked up between the thumb and forefinger. Four sticks at a time are removed from this group and set down, until four or fewer remain between the left thumb and forefinger. The ritual numbers obtained are:

One stick remaining	3
Two sticks remaining	3
Three sticks remaining	3
Four sticks remaining	2

(Right-hand group ≡ 3)
(Right-hand group ≡ 2)
(Right-hand group ≡ 1)
(Right-hand group ≡ 4)

The numbers in parentheses to the right are the results of a checking operation. To perform this checking operation, the sticks remaining from the left-hand group are placed between the second and third fingers of the left hand, and the right-hand group is picked up between thumb and forefinger. Four sticks at a time are removed from this group and added to the pile. If one stick remained from the left-hand group, there should be three remaining sticks from the right-hand group. Similarly, two remaining from the left-hand group should give two remaining from the right-hand group, and so forth. At the end of this operation, there should be either five (ritual number 3) or nine (ritual number 2) sticks in the various slots of the left hand. These are set aside, and the rest of the (forty or forty-four) sticks are again shaken and sorted into two groups. This time, the ritual numbers obtained are:

One stick remaining	3
Two sticks remaining	3
Three sticks remaining	2
Four sticks remaining	2

(Right-hand group ≡ 2)
(Right-hand group ≡ 1)
(Right-hand group ≡ 4)
(Right-hand group ≡ 3)

The two ritual numbers obtained from these two sorts are added together and remembered. The four or eight sticks remaining from the second sort are added to the five or nine from the first sort, and the rest of the sticks are sorted a final time. The ritual numbers from the second and third sorts are the same.

When all three numbers are totaled, a 6, 7, 8, or 9 has been obtained. The whole operation is performed six times to cast a hexagram. Undoubtedly this appears incredibly complicated to the novice. The numbers 2 and 3 are, however, obtained by a perfectly logical though seemingly arbitrary procedure from the numbers of sticks. The act of counting and sorting the sticks quickly becomes almost automatic; and if it is done deliberately with a straight back and deep diaphragmatic breathing, it is a useful meditation device that invariably establishes the intuitive state of consciousness prerequisite to proper interpretation of the oracle.

[2] Tao 道 is the Way. As in English, this means both a road and a means or method. In Chinese, it means the correct way. Te 德 is Virtue and means, all at once, goodness, characteristics, and power. Arthur Waley translates 道德 "The Way and its Power."

[3] Yin and Yang are not visible to the naked human eye, but we can see their manifestations Ch'ien (Heaven, toughness) and K'un (Earth, softness). Similarly, though we cannot see the six seats (positions) in the hexagrams (whose natures alternate Yin-Yang, Yin-Yang, Yin-Yang), we can see the Yin and Yang lines that occupy them by turn.

[4] This counting backward evidently refers to Fu Hsi's arrangement of the trigrams about the Tai Chi:

THE EIGHT ELEMENTS OR TRIGRAMS
Another Version by King Wen

[6] They asked once, and got a boy named Ch'ang-nan.
They asked once, and got a girl named Ch'ang-nu.
They asked twice, and got a boy named Chung-nan.
They asked twice, and got a girl named Chung-nü.
They asked three times, and got a boy named Hsiao-nan.
They asked three times, and got a girl named Hsiao-nü.

The Interaction of Eight Basic Elements or Trigrams of the Universe as seen by Fu Hsi

[5] King Wen arranged the trigrams differently:

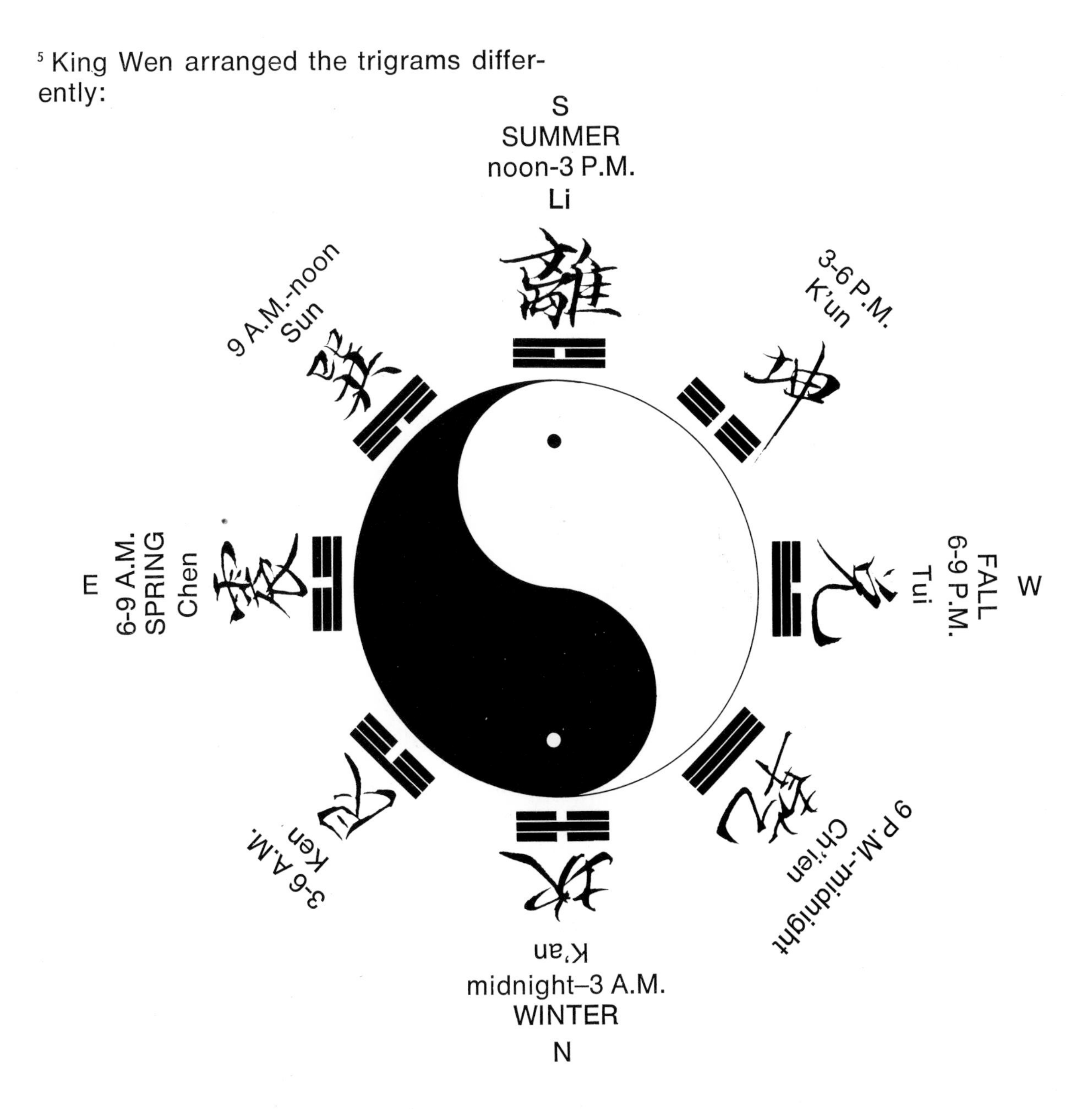

Table of Contents: The I Ching

23. Po[1]	Splitting Apart	Splitting Apart	to strip off, to peel
24. Fu[4]	Returning	Return (The Turning Point)	to return, again
25. Wu[2] Wang[4]	Here and Now	Innocence (The Unexpected)	to goof, without falseness
26. Ta[4] Hsü[4]	Great Husbandry	Taming Power of the Great	great rearing, big animals
27. I[2]	Jaws	Corners of the Mouth	jaw, chin
28. Ta[4] Kuo[4]	Too Big	Preponderance of the Great	great passing through, vast mistake
29. K'an[3]	The Pit	The Abysmal (Water)	pit, watery trap
30. Li[2]	Clinging Beauty	The Clinging, Fire	to separate, brightness
31. Hsien[2]	Inducing Movement	Influence (Wooing)	all, to unite
32. Heng[2]	The Constant	Duration	constant, cyclical
33. Tun[4]	Getting Away	Retreat	hiding, fleeing
34. Ta[4] Chuang[4]	Great Power	Power of the Great	great strength, big and healthy
35. Chin[4]	Advancing	Progress	to advance, to increase
36. Ming[2] I[2]	Injured Brilliance	Darkening of the Light	light darkening, brightness exterminated
37. Chia[1] Jen[2]	The Family	The Family (The Clan)	family of man, home of man
38. K'uei[1]	Dissensus	Opposition	separated, in opposition
39. Chien[3]	The Stumbling Block	Obstruction	trouble, lame
40. Chiai[3]	Loosening	Deliverance	to untie, to loosen
41. Sun[3]	Subtraction	Decrease	to spoil, loss
42. I[4]	Addition	Increase	benefit, to profit
43. Kuai[4]	Resolution	Break-Through (Resoluteness)	to decide, parted
44. Kou[4]	Chance Encounter	Coming to Meet	to meet by chance, to couple

45. Ts'ui^{4}	Creating Unity	Gathering Together (Massing)	common bond, collection
46. Sheng^{1}	Climbing Up	Pushing Upward	to arise, to promote
47. K'un^{4}	Getting Stuck	Oppression (Exhaustion)	surrounded by, distress
48. Ching^{3}	The Well	The Well	well, pit
49. Ke^{2}	Revolution	Revolution (Molting)	skin, transformation
50. Ting^{3}	The Sacrificial Caldron	The Caldron	sacrificial caldron, empire
51. Chen^{4}	The Blast	The Arousing (Shock, Thunder)	to shake, to terrify
52. Ken^{4}	Holding the Center	Keeping Still, Mountain	to stop, a limit
53. Chien^{4}	Gradually	Development (Gradual Progress)	gradually, to flow
54. Kuei^{1} Mei^{4}	Marrying Off Little Sister	The Marrying Maiden	younger sister's return, her marriage
55. Feng^{1}	Lushness	Abundance (Fullness)	luxuriant, abundant
56. Lü^{3}	The Stranger	The Wanderer	to travel, guest
57. Sun^{4}	Flexibility	The Gentle (The Penetrating, Wind)	bland, southeast
58. Tui^{4}	Pleasure	The Joyous, Lake	exchange, to weigh
59. Huan^{4}	Vaporizing	Dispersion (Dissolution)	scattered, to expand
60. Chieh^{2}	Restraint	Limitation	bamboo joint, chastity
61. Chung^{1} Fu^{2}	Inward Charisma	Inner Truth	central confidence, certain trust within
62. Hsiao^{3} Kuo^{4}	Too Small	Preponderance of the Small	small passing through, insignificant mistake
63. Chi^{4} Chi^{4}	Already Done	After Completion	since aid, already complete
64. Wei^{4} Chi^{4}	Not Yet Done	Before Completion	not being aided, not yet complete

*These are romanizations of the Chinese pronunciation, using the so-called Wade-Giles system. These guides to the Chinese pronunciation are of limited usefulness, but with them an educated stab may be made. There are, for example, several dozen words pronounced ch'ien. The superscripted number specifies the tone in which the word is to be pronounced, and would distinguish hexagram 1 (in the second tone) from hexagram 15 (in the first). Still, since there are a dozen or so different, common words pronounced exactly alike, confusion remains. Possibly, Chinese was phonetically richer in the twelfth century B.C. At any rate, a Chinese-speaking person now would find a passage of classical Chinese quite unintelligible if read to him aloud unless he happened to recognize it.

In general, the Wade-Giles system is phonetic. J and ih are pronounced like an r; each vowel is pronounced separately. The apostrophes after ch', ts', t', k', and p' merely signify the aspiration which would be normal English pronunciation of these sounds; without apostrophes, they are pronounced more softly so that ch sounds like j, ts like dz, t like d, k like a hard g, and p like b. Tone 1 is normal; tone 2 rises at the end like a question; tone 3 drops and rises like a dramatically incredulous question ("Whaaaat?"), and tone 4 sounds like a curt command.

†The most commonly used version of the I in America today is the translation by Cary Baynes from the German translation by Richard Wilhelm in 1923 (New York: Pantheon Books, 1950). We display the Wilhelm-Baynes translations here for purposes of comparison and recognition.

**These are the kinds of meanings which would occur to an educated Chinese if he encountered the word out of context, perhaps in a newspaper. It should be remembered that the I Ching has played, for three thousand years, a central role in the Chinese language. Just as an educated American would recognize a whole verse from Shakespeare or the Bible as a classical passage, these individual words possess, as part of their modern meaning, the connotation of the hexagram they describe.

1
Strength

heaven above
heaven below

Strength is primal,
In the groove of the
Way,
Profitable,
And steady.

6. The overconfident dragon has regret.
5. The dragon flies in heaven. Seeing the great man will be profitable.
4. Leaping about in the chasm. Not his fault.
3. All day the Superior Man is busy. In the evening, he is still careful and alert to danger. Therefore, he is faultless.
2. See the dragon in the field. Seeing the great man will be profitable.
1. The hidden dragon does not act.
All six. See a group of dragons with no leader. Good luck.

2
Submission

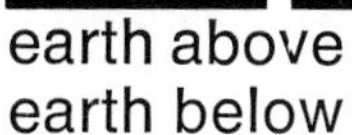
earth above
earth below

Submission is primal,
In the groove of the Way,
Profitable,
And has the steadiness of a mare.
The Superior Man first loses,
Then finds his way
By following his master.
He profits by attaining friends
In the south and west—
He loses friends
In the east and north.
His steadiness is secure—
Good luck.

6. Dragons fight in the void. Their blood is black and yellow.
5. Yellow clothing. Steadiness brings good luck.
4. Tied up in a bag. Not his fault, but not his glory.
3. Concealing his abilities, he goes ahead steadily. In case he is on official business, he doesn't strive for success, but sees things through to completion.
2. Straight, square, great, and conscious. Anything will be profitable.
1. Stepping on frost. Eternal ice will come.
All six. Eternal steadiness will be profitable.

3 A Difficult Stage

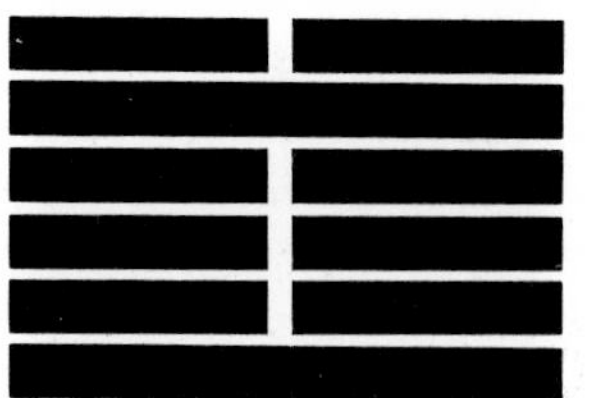

water above
thunder below

A difficult stage is primal,
In the groove of the Way,
Profitable,
And steady.
He doesn't have to go anywhere;
It is profitable
To consolidate his position.

6. The wagon is disconnected from the horse. He weeps tears of blood.
5. A difficult stage in dispensing bounty. A little steadiness brings good luck; great steadiness brings disaster.
4. Like riding a horse and chariot, shyly, like begging her to marry him. Good luck everywhere. Anything will be profitable.
3. Chasing deer with no guide, finding himself in the middle of the woods, the Superior Man knows he should stay where he is and abandon the chase. Going on would get nowhere.
2. Treating immaturity gently brings and chariot in all directions. Like a seducer after a girl who maintains her chastity and doesn't yield. After ten years, then she yields.
1. When things are uncertain, maintaining steadiness is profitable, and consolidating one's position is profitable.

4
Immaturity

mountain above
water below

Immaturity is
groovy.
I don't seek the kid,
He seeks me out.
I answer his first
cast,
But if he pesters
me three times,
He gets boring.
I don't teach bores.
Steadiness is
profitable.

6. Attacking is not a profitable way to deal with immaturity. It is profitable to prevent attack.
5. Fresh immaturity brings good luck.
4. Tangled immaturity gets one nowhere.
3. Don't take the girl who freaks out when she sees a man's money. Nothing will be profitable.
2. Treating immaturity gently brings good luck. Knowing how to take a woman brings good luck. The son can take charge of the family.
1. It is profitable to use punishment to enlighten immaturity, but using too much punishment gets nowhere.

5
Waiting

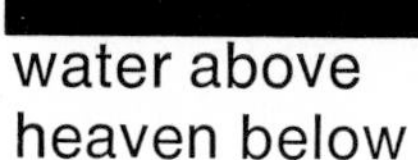

water above
heaven below

Waiting is
charismatic;
Bright and groovy.
Steadiness brings
good luck.
Crossing the great
river is profitable.

6. He goes into the cave, and has three surprise guests. Treating them respectfully brings ultimate good luck.
5. Waiting at the feast. Steadiness brings good luck.
4. Waiting in blood. He leaves the cave.
3. Waiting in the mud. That brings on the attack.
2. Waiting in the sand. Gossip, but ultimate good luck.
1. Waiting in the suburbs. Using constant things will be profitable.

6
Contention

heaven above
water below

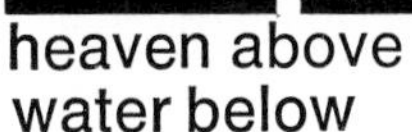

Contention has charisma.
Snuffing out the hassle in the middle
Brings good luck;
Contending through to the end
Brings disaster.
Seeing the great man is profitable.
Crossing the great river is profitable.

6. In case he is awarded a leather belt, it will be taken away three times by the end of the morning.
5. Contention brings the greatest good luck.
4. He can't resolve the contention, so he returns and submits to fate. Peaceful steadiness brings good luck.
3. He cultivates the ancient virtues steadily. Trouble starts, but in the end, good luck. In case he is on official business, he will accomplish nothing.
2. He can't resolve the contention. He returns to his home town where he and three hundred families escape harm.
1. He doesn't demand completion. Gossip, but ultimate good luck.

7
The Army

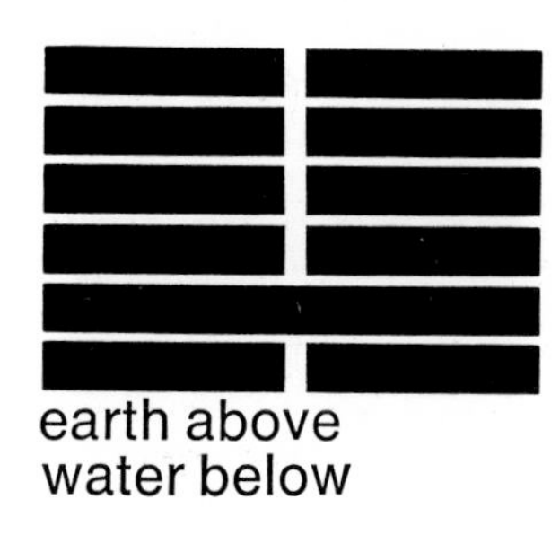

earth above
water below

The army has the
steadiness
Of a sage.
Good luck,
No fault.

6. The destiny of a great prince is to found nations and head clans. Don't use small men.
5. There are beasts in the field. He profits by holding his tongue, so that he is not at fault. The oldest son is in command, while the younger ones cart away the bodies. Steadiness brings disaster.
4. The army holds its horses. It is not at fault.
3. If the army carries truckloads of bodies, it is a disaster.
2. He is in the middle of the army. He has good luck; nothing is his fault. He returns three times to receive honors.
1. The army must have proper organization. Otherwise, disaster threatens.

8
Maintaining Unity

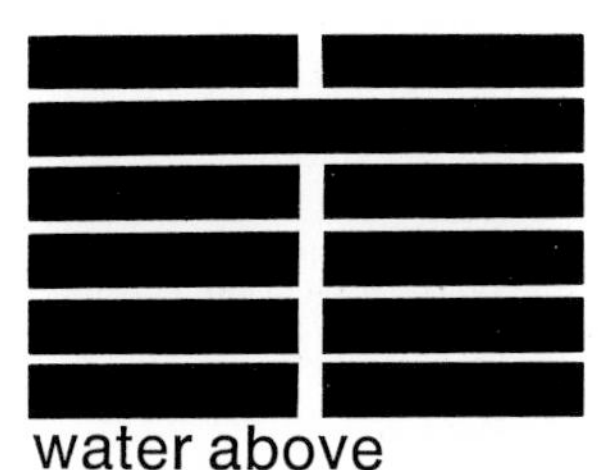

water above
earth below

Maintaining unity
brings good luck.
Examine the primal
cast for eternal
steadiness.
It is not at fault.
The restless come
from afar,
And disaster
befalls the late
husband.

6. Maintaining unity with no leadership brings disaster.
5. Gloriously maintaining unity, the king heads his quarry in three directions but loses it straight ahead. He failed to notify the villagers. Good luck.
4. Ethnic integration. Steadiness brings good luck.
3. Maintaining unity with evil men.
2. Maintaining unity from within. Steadiness brings good luck.
1. There is charisma. Unity is maintained faultlessly, for there is the charisma of a clay bowl. Ultimately, good luck from without.

9
Small Husbandry

wind above
heaven below

Small husbandry is in the groove of the Way.
Thick clouds but no rain
From our western region.

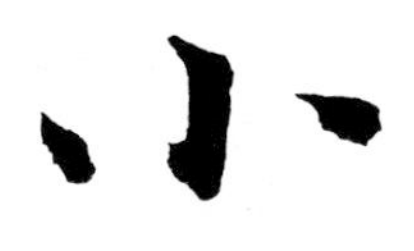

6. The rains come, and everything is at rest. Virtue continues to increase. The steady girl courts disaster. If the Superior Man goes forth when the moon is nearly full, he risks disaster.
5. Charisma is a leash, and his richness encompasses his neighbors.
4. Charisma brings great courage and eliminates fear. There is no fault.
3. The spoke flies off the wheel of the vehicle. The couple is squabbling.
2. Compelling return brings good luck.
1. He goes back to doing his thing. How could anything be his fault? Good luck.

10
Stepping

heaven above
lake below

Stepping on the
tiger's tail—
It doesn't bite the
man.
Groovy.

6. He watches his step and analyzes the future. Everything is fulfilled. Primal good luck.
5. Stepping resolutely. Steadiness brings danger.
4. Stepping on the tiger's tail with fearful apprehensiveness brings ultimate good luck.
3. The one-eyed man still sees, and the lame man still walks. He who steps on the tiger's tail gets bit. Disaster. But the sergeant can do the job of his great commander.
2. Level stepping on the level path. The steadiness of a detached man brings good luck.
1. Stepping simply, he goes forth. It isn't his fault.

11 Thriving

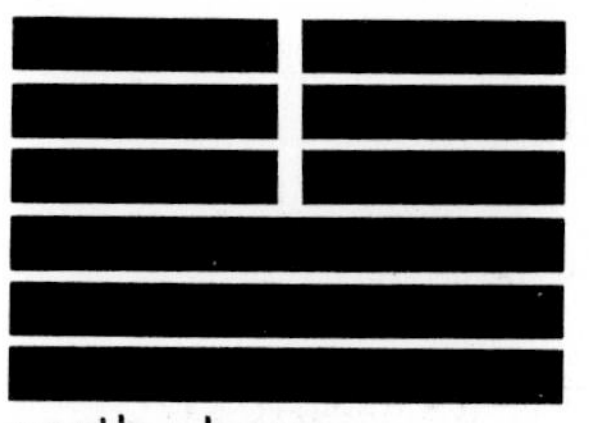

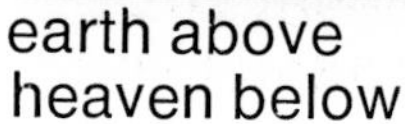

earth above
heaven below

Thriving.
The small go,
The great come:
Good luck.
Groovy.

6. The wall of the city disintegrates. Don't use force; keep order in your own city. Steadiness brings regret.
5. The Emperor Yee gave away his daughter and earned happiness. The fortune of good luck.
4. Go elegantly but not ostentatiously. Deal with your neighbor not with pressure but with charisma.
3. Every plain is followed by a hill. Every departure is followed by an arrival. Steadiness in the face of difficulty is no fault. Don't despair of your own charisma; enjoy the happiness of the here and now.
2. Treat clods gently. No matter how far, cross the water. Ignore the difficulty of great distance and the trap of friendship. Then you can steer the middle path.
1. When you pull up crabgrass, the sod comes along. Marching forth brings good luck.

12
Stagnation

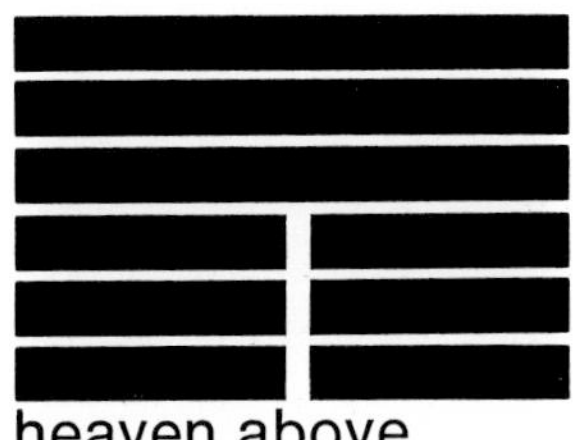

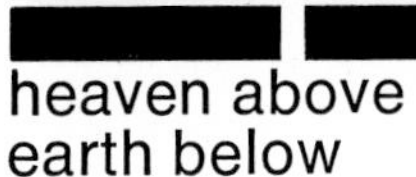

heaven above
earth below

Stagnation.
Evil men are
unprofitable
For the Superior
Man's steadiness.
The great go,
The small come.

6. Overcoming stagnation. Formerly stagnant, finally joyful.
5. Stagnation is ending. Good luck for the Superior Man. Finished, finished. Propped up like a mulberry shoot.
4. There is fate, it isn't his fault. The people around are made beautiful and happy.
3. Concealed shame.
2. Good luck for inferior brown-noses. Stagnation for the Superior Man. Groovy.
1. When you pull up crabgrass, the sod comes along. Steadiness brings good luck. Groovy.

13
Brotherhood

heaven above
flame below

Brotherhood in the back country is groovy.
Crossing the great river is profitable.
For the Superior Man,
Steadiness is profitable.

6. Brotherhood in the suburbs is no fault.
5. Brotherhood. At first, cry and moan; later, laugh. The great masses can join together.
4. Climbing the city wall but withholding the attack brings good luck.
3. He throws his weapons in the bushes and climbs up the high hill. He is beaten down for three years.
2. Brotherhood with one's own cousins brings trouble.
1. Brotherhood at the gate is no fault.

14
Affluence

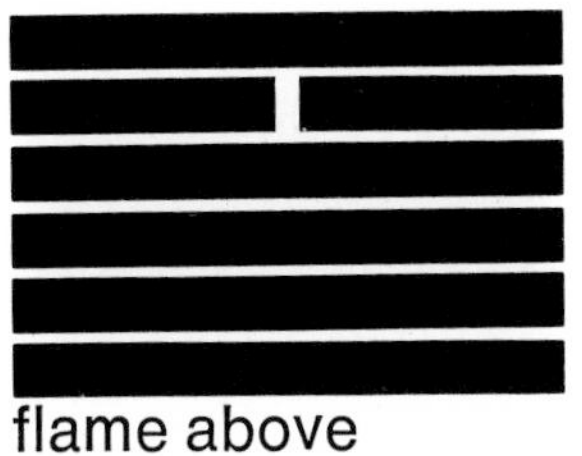

flame above
heaven below

Affluence is primal
And in the groove
of the Way.

6. The blessings of heaven bring good luck. Anything will be profitable.
5. Relevant charisma and a dignified bearing bring good luck.
4. Concealing affluence is no fault.
3. A prince can contribute to the emperor, but the inferior man cannot.
2. A big truck to load. If he has somewhere to go, it is not his fault.
1. Not dealing with evil avoids fault. Awareness of difficulty avoids fault.

15
Humility

earth above
mountain below

Humility is groovy.
The Superior Man
sees things
through to
completion.

6. Crowing about humility. It is profitable to march the army to conquer the city and nation.
5. Not using resources for show, but for constructive purposes. Anything will be profitable.
4. Anything is profitable for the humble man.
3. Hard work and humility. The Superior Man sees things through to completion. Good luck.
2. Crowing about humility. Steadiness brings good luck.
1. The humble Superior Man uses humility to cross the great river. Good luck.

16
Satisfaction

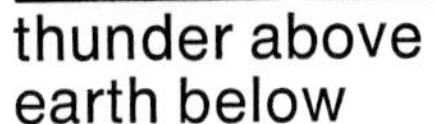

thunder above
earth below

Satisfaction.
Consolidating
positions
And unleashing
armies
Are profitable
things to do.

6. Dark satisfaction. If finally altered, this is no fault.
5. Steadiness brings sickness, but no death.
4. Affluence from satisfaction. Don't doubt your friends who gather hair like barrettes.
3. Looking up to others for satisfaction brings regret. Hesitation brings regret.
2. Solid as a rock, he doesn't wait all day. Steadiness brings good luck.
1. Crowing about satisfaction brings disaster.

17
Following

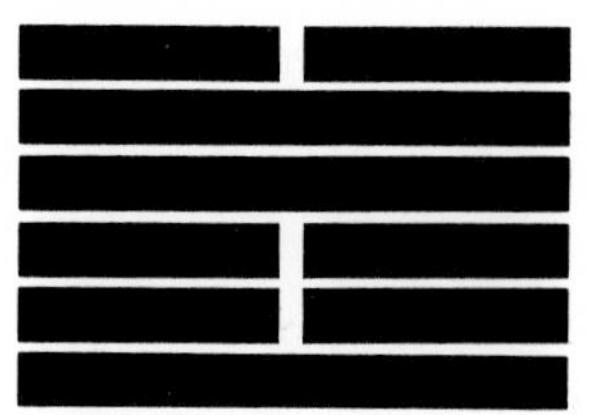

lake above
thunder below

Primal grooving.
Steadiness is
profitable.
It is not his fault.

6. Clinging tight, his followers are tied to him. The king makes a sacrifice in the mountains of the west.
5. The charisma of excellence brings the highest good luck.
4. Steadily attracting followers brings disaster. Charisma in the path to brilliance—how could this be a fault?
3. Clinging to the man loses the small boy. Following gains what is sought. Maintaining steadiness is profitable.
2. Clinging to the small boy loses the man.
1. Values change, but steadiness brings good luck. Going outside and communicating will be productive.

18
Festering

mountain above
wind below

Primal grooving.
Crossing the great river is profitable.
Three days before the beginning;
Three days after the beginning.

6. He does not serve the authorities, but something higher, instead.
5. Setting straight father's festering brings glory.
4. Tolerate father's festering generously. Going on, one sees regret.
3. Setting straight father's festering brings small regret but not great fault.
2. Setting straight mother's festering. Don't be too steady.
1. Setting straight father's festering. If he can depend on his son, he is not at fault. Danger, but ultimate good luck.

19
Going There

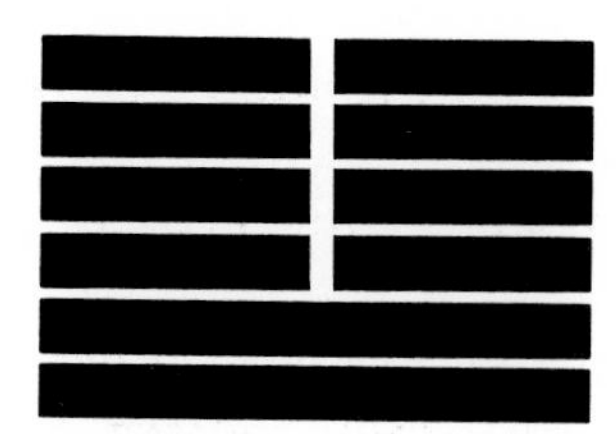

earth above
lake below

Primal grooving.
Steadiness is profitable.
In the eighth moon, disaster.

6. Going there generously brings good luck. There is no fault.
5. Going there knowingly is appropriate for a great king. Good luck.
4. Going there wholeheartedly is no fault.
3. Going there with sweet talk. Nothing will be profitable. If he has sufficient concern, it won't be his fault.
2. They all go there together. Good luck. Anything will be profitable.
1. They all go there together. Steadiness brings good luck.

24
Returning

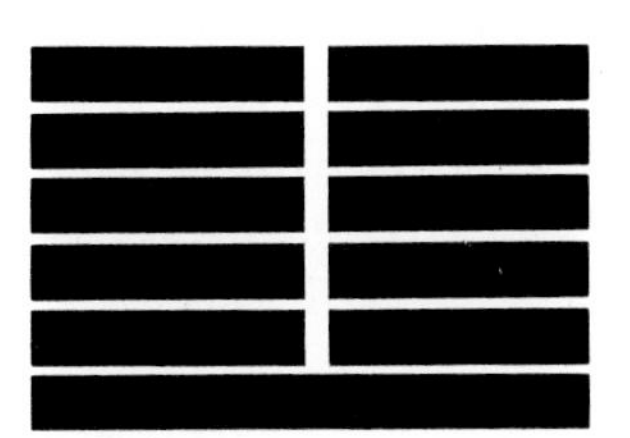

earth above
thunder below

Returning is groovy
Going and coming
with no sickness:
Friends come, not
at fault.
Going and
coming—
Back and forth—
On the way;
Returning a week
later.
Going somewhere
is profitable.

6. Returning astray. Disaster. There will be a calamity and trouble. Armies set marching now will ultimately suffer great defeats; the poor ruler will not recover for ten years.
5. Solid returning. No fault.
4. Walking centered, returning alone.
3. Repeated returning. The danger is not his fault.
2. Returning, taking it easy. Good luck.
1. Returning from nearby. Regret is unnecessary. Greatest good luck.

25
Here and Now

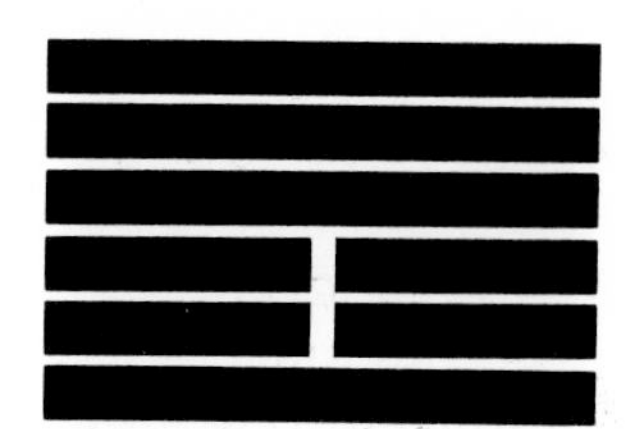

heaven above
thunder below

Primal grooving.
Steadiness is profitable,
But if his mind wanders, he's in trouble.
Going ahead is unprofitable.

6. Walking in the here and now; even then disaster. It will not be profitable.
5. Psychosomatic ailment. He needs no medicine, just joy.
4. Steadiness is okay. He is not at fault.
3. In the here and now, disaster. He ties his cow to a tree—finders keepers, losers weepers.
2. Planting, not planning the harvest; harvesting, not counting the profit. It is profitable to have somewhere to go.
1. In the here and now, going ahead. Good luck.

26 Great Husbandry

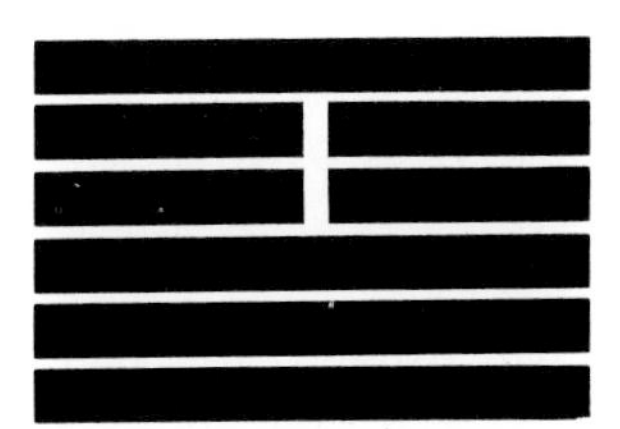

mountain above
heaven below

Steadiness is profitable.
Not eating at home brings good luck.
Crossing the great river is profitable.

6. The freeway to Heaven. Groovy.
5. The tusks of the gelded boar. Good luck.
4. Training the young bull. Good luck.
3. Chasing a good horse. Difficulty is profitable. Steady, daily practice in riding and defense will make it profitable to have somewhere to go.
2. The axle of the carriage is loose.
1. Danger. Stop.

27
Jaws

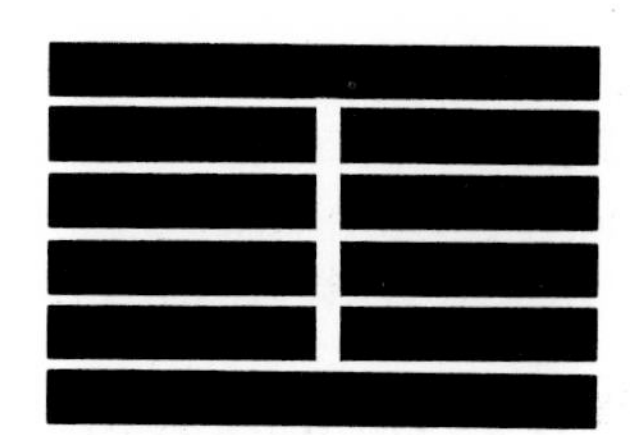

mountain above
thunder below

Steadiness brings
good luck.
See how the jaws
try to fill the mouth.

6. Aware of the danger from nourishment. Good luck. It is profitable to cross the great river.
5. Abandon your normal way and get behind steadiness. Good luck. It is forbidden to cross the great river.
4. Lifting your face. Good luck. The tiger glares sharply with desire driving, driving. Not his fault.
3. Abandon nourishment. Steady disaster. Do nothing for ten years, for it will be unprofitable.
2. Lifting your face, abandoning your normal way, and raising your chin in supplication makes for a disastrous expedition.
1. Give up your tortoise, and stare at me open-mouthed. Disaster.

28
Too Big

lake above
wind below

Too big, the beam collapses.
Going somewhere is profitable.
Groovy.

6. To cross the river, go under water. Disaster, but not his fault.
5. The withered willow sprouts flowers. The old woman goes home with a potent man. No fault, but no glory.
4. Strengthening the beam brings good luck. Looking to others for help gets nowhere.
3. The beam sags. Disaster.
2. The withered willow sprouts a root. The old man takes a young girl home. Nothing is unprofitable.
1. Put it on a white mat. No fault.

29
The Pit

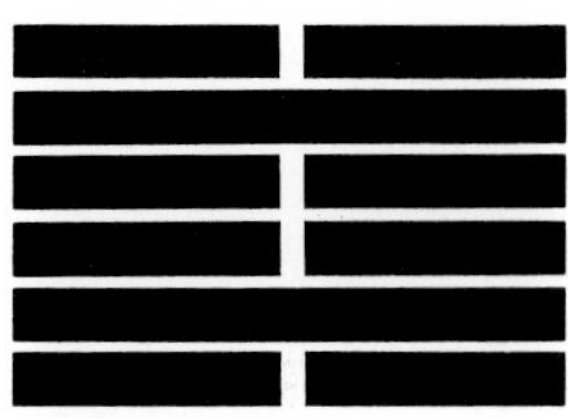

water above
water below

The pit repeated.
He has charisma, and holds his center.
Steady behavior is appropriate.

6. Bound with black ropes, the thorns multiplying—for three years he will not be happy. Disaster.
5. The pit is not full, just level. Not its fault.
4. A jug of wine and a basket of food—both clay. Sneak in through the window. Ultimately, it's no fault of yours.
3. Coming to the pit is dangerous. Nap and fall into the trap. Don't do it.
2. The pit is dangerous. Seek small gains.
1. Used to the pit, go into a hole. Disaster.

30 Clinging Beauty

flame above
flame below

Steadiness is profitable. Groovy. Husbanding cows brings good fortune.

6. The ruler sends him marching forth to conquer. He gets good things and breaks the enemy leaders—but not the followers, for it's not their fault.
5. Tears flow like sighing, lamenting like. Good luck.
4. Sudden coming. Like burning, death, abandonment, like.
3. The sun sets. Instead of playing his drum and singing, he emits octagenarian groans. Disaster.
2. Bright sunlight. Greatest good luck.
1. Confused steps, but if he is reverent it is not his fault.

31
Inducing Movement

lake above
mountain below

Inducing movement is groovy
Steadiness is profitable.
Taking the girl home brings good luck.

6. Talk.
5. Inducing movement in his back, he is not at fault.
4. Steady good luck; regret disappears. If he vacillates, he will induce movement in his friends.
3. Inducing movement in the thighs, keeping hold of followers, and going ahead brings disaster.
2. Inducing movement in the calves brings disaster; abiding brings good luck.
1. Inducing movement in the big toe.

32 The Constant

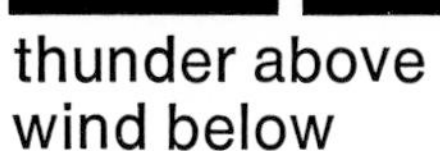

thunder above
wind below

The constant is groovy.
He is not at fault.
Steadiness is profitable.
Going somewhere is profitable.

6. Constant vacillation brings disaster.
5. The virtue of constancy. This steadiness brings the wife good luck, the husband disaster.
4. No game in the field.
3. Not constantly following virtue is a shameful thing. Steadiness brings regret.
2. Regret disappears.
1. Deep constancy. Steadiness brings disaster. Nothing is profitable.

33 Getting Away

heaven above
mountain below

Getting away is groovy. Steadiness is a little profitable.

6. Getting away by means of detachment. Anything will be profitable.
5. Getting away properly. Steadiness brings good luck.
4. Deliberately getting away brings good luck to the Superior Man, disaster to the Inferior Man.
3. Tangled getting away—the danger of sickness. But, if he takes good care of his concubines and subordinates, he will have good luck.
2. Held tightly with tough leather. Nobody can break it loose.
1. Getting away from behind is dangerous. He doesn't have to go anywhere.

34 Great Power

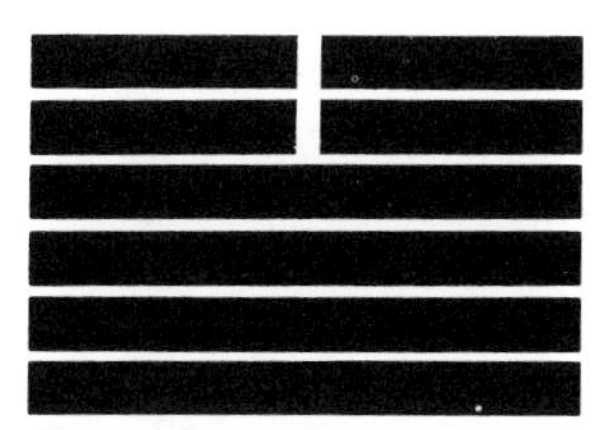

thunder above
heaven below

Steadiness is profitable.

6. The goat butts up against the hedge so that he can't retreat or advance. Nothing will be profitable. Difficulty, but ultimate good luck.
5. Losing the goat easily, with no regret.
4. Steadiness brings good luck. Regret disappears when he breaks loose from the entangling hedge. Strength in the axle of the great vehicle.
3. The Inferior Man uses all the power he has; the Superior Man does not. Steadiness brings danger. The goat butts up against the hedge so that his horns are entangled.
2. Steadiness brings good luck.
1. Power in the toes. Marching forth brings disaster, which has charisma.

35
Advancing

flame above
earth below

The eminent
nobleman
Has many great
horses and a lot of
property.
Three receptions
under one blazing
sun.

6. Advance with horns lowered only in order to smash your own city. Awareness of danger brings good luck and is not a fault. Steadiness brings regret.
5. Regret disappears. Loss and gain don't matter. Going ahead meets with good luck. Anything will be profitable.
4. Advance like a bum. Steadiness brings danger.
3. Consensus. Regret disappears.
2. Advance like alertly, like. Steadiness brings good luck. Receive great happiness from the Queen Mother.
1. Advance, but get stopped. Steadiness brings good fortune. If there is no charisma, cool it and you won't be at fault.

36
Injured Brilliance

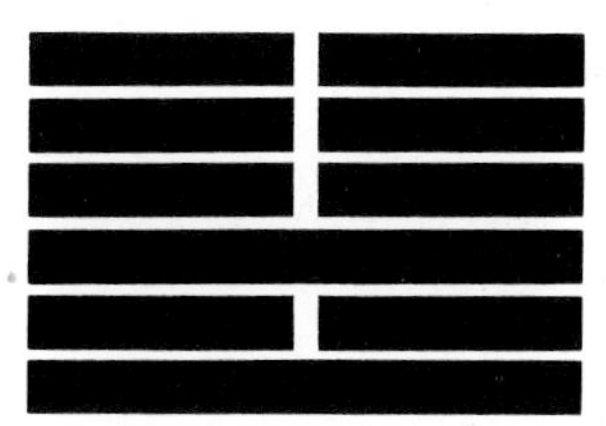

earth above
flame below

Steadiness in the
face of tremendous
difficulty
Is profitable.

6. Uninjured brilliance first climbs to Heaven, then plunges to earth.
5. Prince Chi's brilliance was injured, but he profited from steadiness.
4. Go into the left side of the belly and reach the heart of injured brilliance. Now he can leave the courtyard through the gate.
3. Injured brilliance on a southern hunt. The great chief is taken. Don't rush; be steady.
2. Injured brilliance in the left thigh. He helps them with the strength of a horse. Good luck.
1. Injured brilliance, flying, lowers the wings. The Superior Man on the road doesn't eat for three days; if he had to go, his host would have a word with him.

37 The Family

wind above
flame below

The steadiness of a woman is profitable.

6. He has charisma, awesome, like. Finally, good luck.
5. The king organizes his family. Don't worry; good luck.
4. Enriching the family brings great good luck.
3. The members of the family are piously regretful and alert. Good luck. Woman and child laugh and chat, but finally, humiliation.
2. Not following her own impulses, but swaying in the back taking care of the food. Steadiness brings good luck.
1. Setting strict regulations and boundaries for the family makes regret disappear.

38
Dissensus

flame above
lake below

Good luck in small things.

6. Dissensus and isolation. See a hog with mud on his shoulders as a truckload of demons. First stretch the bow, then release it; he is no robber, but a boyfriend. Go ahead and meet the rain. Good luck.
5. Regret disappears. The leader bites through the skin. When he goes ahead, how can it be his fault?
4. Dissensus and isolation, meeting the best husband with mutual charisma. Danger threatens, but it isn't his fault.
3. See the vehicle dragged back, the ox halted, a man with his hair and nose clipped off. No beginning sees it through to the end.
2. Encountering his lord in a narrow path wasn't his fault.
1. Regret disappears. If you lose your horse, don't chase it; it will come back by itself. Seeing evil men isn't your fault.

39
The Stumbling Block

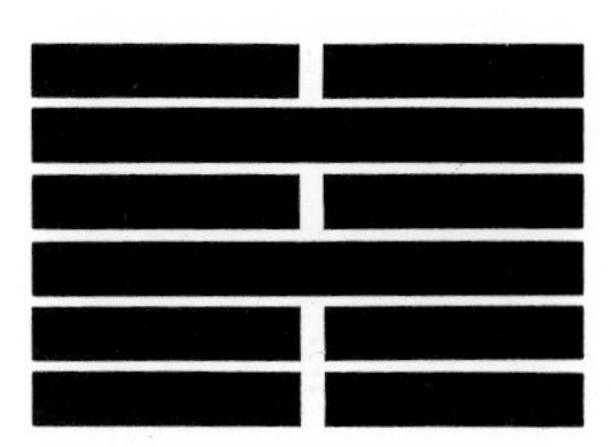

water above
mountain below

The west and south
are profitable,
The east and north
are unprofitable.
Steadiness brings
good luck.

6. The stumbling block going; great good luck coming. Seeing the great man will be profitable.
5. A great stumbling block, but friends arrive.
4. Stumbling block going; connection coming.
3. Stumbling block going; return coming.
2. The king's servant stumbling on the stumbling block. But he is not the reason.
1. The stumbling block going; glory coming.

40
Loosening

thunder above
water below

The west and south
are profitable.
If there is nowhere
to go,
Going back brings
good luck.
If there is some-
where to go,
Doing it quickly
brings good luck.

6. The prince fires a shot at the hawk on the high wall and gets it. Anything will be profitable.
5. The Superior Man alone can facilitate good luck; this gives him charisma for inferior men.
4. Loosening his attachments—friends come to him, then he has charisma.
3. The man who carries his baggage on his back and still rides attracts thieves.
2. He gets three foxes in the field and gains a yellow arrow. Steadiness brings good luck.
1. It isn't his fault.

41
Subtraction

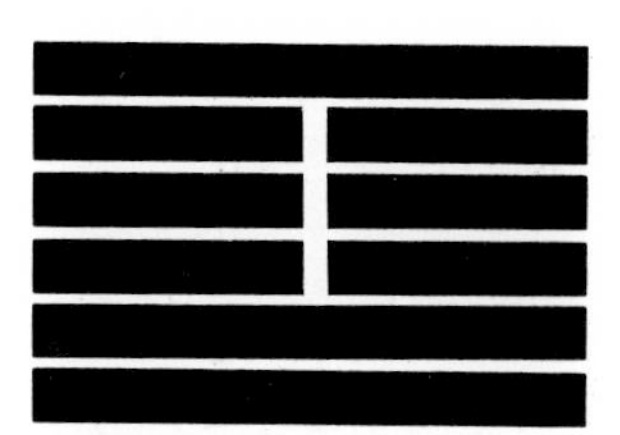

mountain above
lake below

Subtraction with
charisma.
Primal good luck.
Not at fault.
Steadiness is
appropriate.
Going somewhere
is profitable.
How to make the
sacrifice?
Using two bowls is
okay.
Groovy.

6. Addition without subtraction is no fault. Steadiness brings good luck. It is profitable to go somewhere, and to get subordinates, but no family.
5. In case he adds 2,100 tortoise shells and accepts no refusal, the greatest good luck.
4. Subtracting illness by forcing joy is no fault.
3. If three people go, one will be subtracted; if one goes, he will find his friend.
2. Steadiness will be profitable, but marching forth will bring disaster. Not subtraction, addition.
1. Subtract below and add above. It is not his fault, but he should also consider how to subtract.

42
Addition

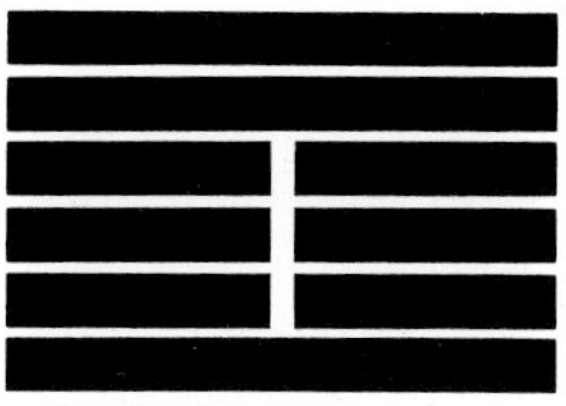

wind above
thunder below

Going somewhere is profitable. Crossing the great river is profitable.

6. Nobody adds, but he stands fast in case of a blow. Inconstancy brings disaster.
5. He has charisma and a giving heart, and does not ask primal good luck.
He has charisma and they reciprocate his virtue.
4. Walking centered, he speaks with the prince. His advice is followed; he can be relied on to move the capital.
3. Addition is brought about by disastrous means, but it is not his fault. He has charisma, and walking centered he speaks with the prince, using his jade seal.
2. In case he adds 2,100 tortoise shells and accepts no refusal, eternal steady good luck. The king's sacrifice to the Lord of Heaven brings good luck.
1. It will be profitable to do a great deed. Primal good luck, and no fault.

43
Resolution

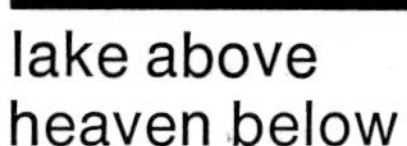
lake above
heaven below

It is proclaimed at
the court of the
king—
A charismatic
announcement of
danger.
Tell your city that
Going to war now
is unprofitable,
But going some-
where is profitable.

6. Without screaming, ultimate disaster.
5. Resolute, like spinach holding to the plain. Resolve to walk centered ensures faultlessness.
4. The skin is off his ass, he can hardly walk. Being pulled like a sheep would eliminate his regret, but though he hears the offer, he doesn't believe it.
3. A strong face brings disaster. The Superior Man has resolve. Resolute, he walks alone in the rain until he is soaked through. He has patience with gossip, for it is not his fault.
2. Seeing the danger, he screams for help all night. But he has an army and shouldn't be afraid.
1. Strength in the big toe stuck out in front. He goes ahead without winning. It is his own fault.

44
Chance Encounter

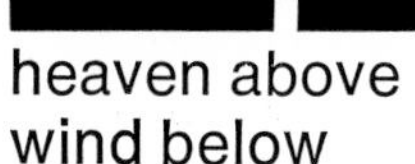

heaven above
wind below

Chance encounter with a tough girl. Do not take this girl home.

6. Chance encounter with his horns lowered. Humiliation, but it is not his fault.
5. The willow leaves cover the melon and hides its beauty. It comes down from heaven.
4. The bag holds no fish. Disaster comes.
3. His ass is skinned so that he can hardly walk. The difficulty is not a great fault.
2. The bag holds fish. No fault, but no profit for guests.
1. Held by a metal brake. Steadiness brings good luck. Having somewhere to go is looking for trouble; even a weak hog can rage about.

45
Creating Unity

lake above
earth below

Creating unity is groovy.
The king takes a tour of the temple.
Seeing the great man is profitable.
Groovy steadiness is profitable.
Giving big animals brings good luck.
Going somewhere is profitable.

6. Loudly expressing frustration with floods of tears is no fault.
5. Creating unity by using his position is no fault. His charisma is not mature, so he needs primal, eternal steadiness to extinguish regret.
4. Great good luck. He is not at fault.
3. Creating unity like moving like sighing. Like not going ahead will be profitable. Going ahead, though not his fault, brings some regret.
2. Being drawn into good luck isn't his fault. There will be charismatic profit in making a summer sacrifice.
1. Having charisma but not seeing things through to completion brings confusion. He screams, but one handclasp makes him laugh. He has no cause for anxiety in going ahead; it isn't his fault.

46
Climbing Up

earth above
wind below

Primal grooving.
It is necessary to
see the great man,
And to be unafraid.
Marching south
brings good luck.

6. Climbing up in the dark. Unremitting steadiness will be profitable.
5. Steadiness brings good luck. Climbing up step by step.
4. The king makes a sacrifice on Mount Ch'i. Good luck and no fault.
3. Climbing up unhindered.
2. Charisma is profitable. Making a summer sacrifice is no fault.
1. Climbing up together. Great good luck.

47
Getting Stuck

lake above
water below

Groovy.
The steadiness of a great man
Brings good luck.
It isn't his fault.

6. Getting stuck in a creeping vine. Stumbling, he says, "If I move, I'll regret it." If he regrets and then drives forward, he will have good luck.
5. His nose and feet are cut off, and he gets stuck in the official uniform. Slowly, he will have the joy of reunion. Surrendering to Heaven will be profitable.
4. Coming very slowly, getting stuck in a golden carriage. He will have regret, but see things through to completion.
3. Getting stuck at a boulder, leaning on thorns. He enters the palace and doesn't see his wife. Disaster.
2. Getting stuck at a feast. The official uniform comes. Making a sacrifice will be profitable. Starting a project brings disaster, but it is not his fault.
1. His ass is stuck in the trunk of a dead tree. He will enter a dark valley and not see anybody for three years.

48 The Well

water above
wind below

The town moved,
but the well
endures.
It loses nothing;
It gains nothing.
They go and come,
back and forth, to
the welling well.
But sometimes
Their poles aren't
long enough,
Or their bottles
break.
Disaster.

6. The well is full to the brim, and they can't cover it. Charisma brings primal good luck.
5. The well is cold. Cold spring water to drink.
4. The well is being lined, but it is not his fault.
3. The well has been cleaned, but they don't use it. Our hearts are sad, for it could be used to supply water. If the king were enlightened, we could share his benefit.
2. The well has a hole, and the perch jump. The bottle is broken and leaks.
1. The well is muddy, and they don't drink—an old well, not even birds.

49
Revolution

lake above
flame below

Revolution
achieves charisma
in mid-morning.
Primal, Groovy,
Steady, and
profitable.
Regret disappears.

6. The Superior Man transforms like a leopard. Small men revolutionize their faces. Action brings disaster, but steadiness brings good luck.
5. The great man transforms like a tiger. He doesn't need to ask the oracle; he has charisma.
4. Regret disappears. He has charisma. Changing administrative organization brings good luck.
3. Action brings disaster. Steady danger. When the revolution has been discussed three times, then it has charisma.
2. In the middle of the morning, then revolution. Action brings good luck, and there will be no fault.
1. Tied up with tough leather.

50 The Sacrificial Caldron

flame above
wind below

Primal good luck.
Groovy.

6. The sacrificial caldron has jade rings. Great good luck. Anything will be profitable.
5. The sacrificial caldron has yellow ears and golden rings. Steadiness will be profitable.
4. The feet of the sacrificial caldron are broken and the prince's meal is spilled all over him. Disaster.
3. The ears of the sacrificial caldron are changed, and moving it is hindered. The flesh of the fat pheasant is not eaten. But the rain comes and regret becomes empty. Ultimate good luck.
2. The sacrificial caldron is full. My enemy is jealous, but he can't do anything to me. Good luck.
1. The sacrificial caldron with its feet turned up. Getting rid of the bad contents is profitable. Taking a concubine in order to have a son is no fault.

51
The Blast

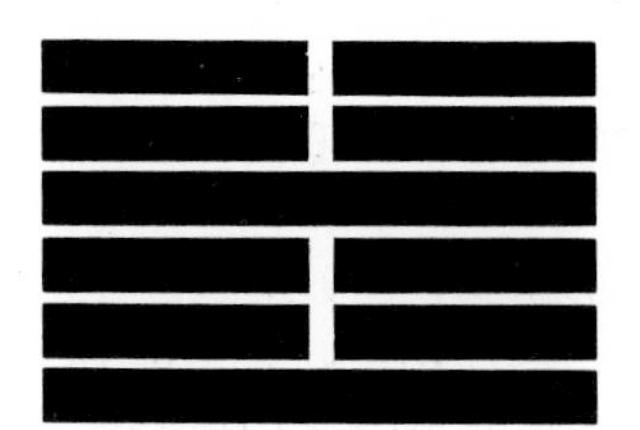

thunder above
thunder below

The blast is groovy.
The blast crashes,
"Ha, ha!"
He chuckles, "Wa,
wa."
The shock terrifies
Everyone for a
hundred miles,
But he doesn't spill
any wine from his
glass.

6. The blast has disrupted everything. He looks around, terrified—going ahead would bring disaster. The blast doesn't affect his own body, but those of his neighbors. That isn't his fault. Any marriage causes gossip.
5. The blast goes and comes. He analyzes the danger. No loss; he has things to do.
4. The blast shoves him into the mud.
3. The blast upsets him. He is blasted into action and is not at fault.
2. The blast is dangerous. Upon analysis, he lets go of things and climbs the nine hills. He doesn't chase the things; they will come in a week.
1. The blast is coming—oh, oh. But then he sings—ha, ha. Good luck.

52 Holding the Center

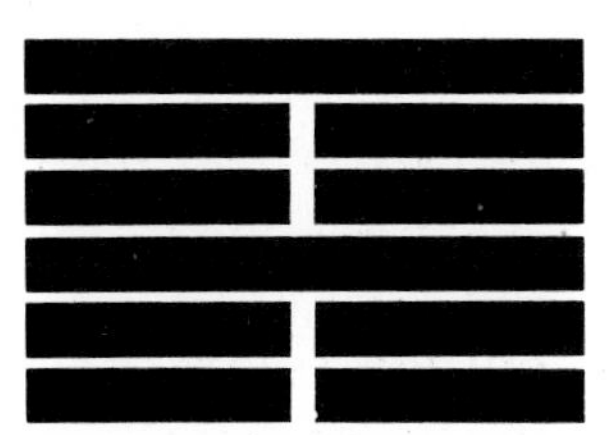

mountain above
mountain below

Back straight,
No sense of body.
Walking in the
yard,
Seeing nobody.
Not at fault.

6. Solidly centered. Good luck.
5. Centered in the mouth. Orderly speech extinguishes regret.
4. Centered body. There is no fault.
3. Bent at the waist, pinching a nerve. There is danger that his heart will broil.
2. Centered in the legs. He cannot save his following, and his heart is sad.
1. Centered in the toes. It is not his fault. Steadiness will be profitable.

53
Gradually

wind above
mountain below

The woman is married off. Good luck. Steadiness is profitable.

6. The wild goose comes gradually to the mainland. Her feathers may be used as an exemplary model. Good luck.
5. The wild goose comes gradually to the mound. For three years the woman doesn't conceive, but in the end nothing can stop her. Good luck.
4. The wild goose gradually comes to the tree. In case she finds a flat branch, she is not at fault.
3. The wild goose comes gradually to the plain. The husband marches off but doesn't return; the wife conceives but bears no child. Disaster. Defending oneself against attack is profitable.
2. The wild goose comes gradually to the cliff. Coming gradually to feast brings good luck.
1. The wild goose comes gradually to the shore. The eligible bachelor is in danger. There is gossip, but it isn't his fault.

54 Marrying Off Little Sister

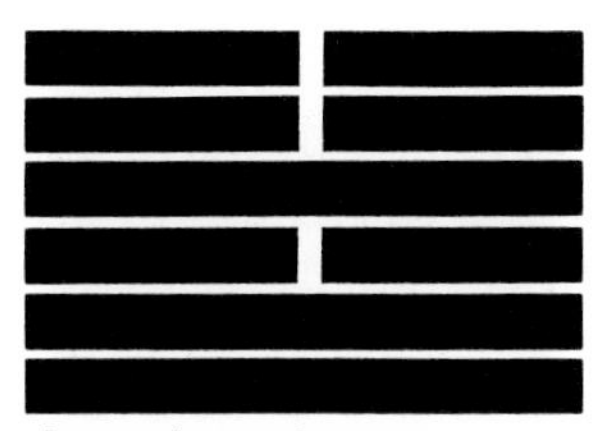

thunder above
lake below

Aggressiveness brings disaster—It is unprofitable.

6. The woman carries a basket, but it's empty. The man stabs a sheep, but it doesn't bleed. Nothing is profitable.
5. The emperor married off his little sister. Her clothes were not as gorgeously embroidered as those of the concubines. The nearly full moon brings good luck.
4. Delay marrying off little sister. There is time for a late marriage.
3. Marrying off the little sister who is a slave brings her back up to concubine.
2. The one-eyed man can still see. The steadiness of the detached man will be profitable. Good luck.
1. Marrying off little sister as a concubine—the lame man still walks. Going ahead brings good luck.

55
Lushness

thunder above
flame below

Lushness is
groovy.
The King
structures it.
Don't worry, it's
appropriate.
The sun is in the
middle of the sky.

6. The full house screens the family. Looking through the gate, he doesn't see anybody. For three years there isn't anybody there. Disaster.
5. Men of enlightenment come and give praise. Good luck.
4. A lush screen. At noon he can see the Little Dipper through it. Meeting the friendly master brings good luck.
3. Lush rain. At noon he can see the Little Dipper through it. He breaks his right arm, but it isn't his fault.
2. A lush screen. At noon, he can see the Little Dipper through it. Going ahead invites mistrust and hostility, but if charisma blooms, good luck.
1. He meets his appropriate master. For ten full days, he is faultless, and going ahead meets with appreciation.

56
The Stranger

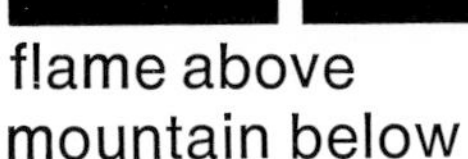

flame above
mountain below

The stranger, a
little groovy.
The steadiness of
a stranger
Brings good luck.

6. The bird burns his nest. The stranger's original laughter turns to screams and tears. It is so easy to lose the cow. Disaster.
5. Shooting at a pheasant. He loses his first arrow, but finally gains fame and high office.
4. The stranger has shelter, money, and equipment, but "my heart is not happy."
3. The stranger burns down the hotel and loses the steadiness of his faithful servants. Danger.
2. The stranger lives in a hotel, carries money, and has faithful servants.
1. The stranger, preoccupied with details, invites disaster.

57
Flexibility

wind above
wind below

Flexibility, a little groovy.
Going somewhere is profitable.
Seeing the great man is profitable.

6. Crawling under the bed, he loses his money and equipment. Steadiness brings disaster.
5. Steadiness brings good luck and regret disappears. Anything will be profitable. No beginning, but he sees things through to completion. For three days before the change and three days after the change good luck.
4. Regret disappears. He gets three foxes in the field.
3. Rigid flexibility brings humiliation.
2. Crawling under the bed. Confused, he tries to send messages to the gods. Good luck. It is not his fault.
1. Both advancing and retreating: the steadiness of a soldier is profitable.

58
Pleasure

lake above
lake below

Pleasure is groovy. Maintaining cool is profitable.

6. Seducing them is pleasurable.
5. Charisma may rip him apart. Danger.
4. Contrived pleasure is not restful. Abandon that sickness and be happy.
3. Forcing pleasure brings disaster.
2. Charismatic pleasure brings good luck. Regret disappears.
1. Harmonious pleasure. Good luck.

59
Vaporizing

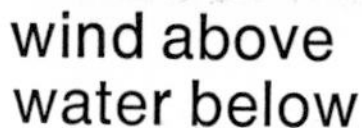
wind above
water below

Vaporizing is groovy.
The king takes a tour of the temple.
Crossing the great river is profitable.
Steadiness is profitable.

6. Vaporize the blood. Staying away is no fault.
5. Vaporize the sweat. Thundering cries vaporize indeed. The king abides, and there is no fault.
4. Vaporize attachments to the faction. Primal good luck. This vaporizing has such nobility that it is incomprehensible to ordinary men.
3. Vaporize your ego. No fault.
2. Vaporizing. He is saved by a life preserver, and regret disappears.
1. Help with the strength of a horse. Good luck.

60 Restraint

water above
lake below

Restraint is groovy.
But strict restraint
is unstable.

6. Rigid restraint. Steadiness brings disaster, but regret disappears.
5. Harmonious restraint brings good luck. Going ahead brings appreciation.
4. Natural restraint is groovy.
3. No restraint, like. But if he is concerned, it is not his fault.
2. Not venturing out through the inner gate brings disaster.
1. Not venturing out through the outer gate is no fault.

61
Inward Charisma

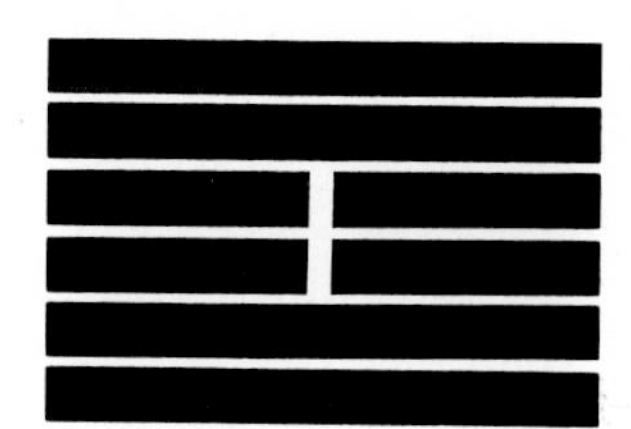

wind above
lake below

Hogs and fish bring good fortune. Crossing the great river is profitable. Steadiness is profitable.

6. The rooster's crowing penetrates to heaven. Steadiness brings disaster.
5. Charismatic connection is no fault.
4. When the moon is almost full, the horse splits off the team. It isn't his fault.
3. He finds his match. Now he beats his drum; now he stops. Now he cries; now he sings.
2. The crane calls from the shadow, and her young respond. "I have a glass of good booze I'll share with you."
1. Preparation brings good luck, but scheming brings anxiety.

62 Too Small

thunder above
mountain below

Too small, but
groovy.
Steadiness is
profitable.
Small things are
okay,
Great ones are not.
The flying bird
drops his voice.
It is not appropriate
to move up.
It is appropriate to
move down.
Great good luck.

6. Not meeting the situation, doing too much. The bird flies too high and meets disaster. That's what is called bringing it on oneself.
5. Thick clouds but no rain from our western region. The prince shoots an arrow and hits the bird hiding in a cave.
4. It is not our fault if we go ahead and meet the situation without doing too much. We must be alert to danger, but not too eternally steady.
3. Not doing too much to prevent danger; it sneaks up behind. Disaster.
2. He doesn't meet his ancestor, he meets his ancestress. He doesn't meet the prince, he meets his minister. It's not his fault.
1. The bird keeps flying. Disaster.

63
Already Done

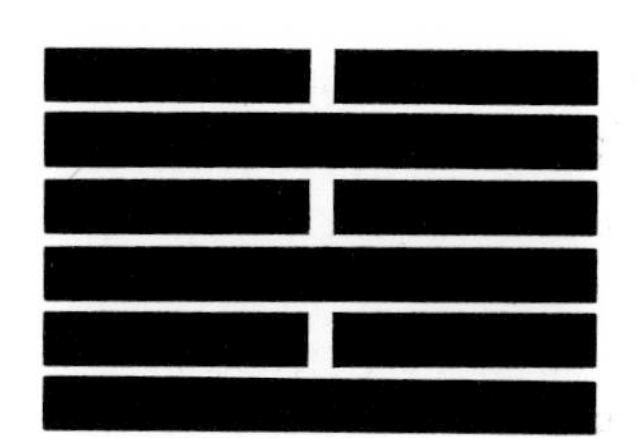

water above
flame below

Groovy.
Steadiness is a little profitable.
At the beginning, good luck;
At the end, confusion.

6. His head is under water. Disaster.
5. The neighbor on the east butchers a cow. This isn't as good as the neighbor on the west, who makes a summer sacrifice and obtains happiness.
4. He has rags to plug leaks and is on guard all day.
3. It took Wu Ting three years to put down the southern barbarians. Don't bother with inferior men.
2. The woman's carriage screen has been stolen. Don't chase it; you'll find it in a week.
1. Braking the wheel when his tail gets wet is no fault.

64
Not Yet Done

flame above
water below

Groovy.
If the little fox,
Not yet across the river,
Gets his tail wet—
There is no profit.

6. Drinking the wine, he has charisma. He is not at fault. But if he dumps it on his head, he has lost his cool.
5. Steadiness brings good luck. The brilliant charisma of the Superior Man brings good luck.
4. Steadiness brings good luck. Regret disappears. It shakes him up to put down the southern barbarians, but for three years he is rewarded with great territories.
3. Not yet done, attack would bring disaster. Crossing the great river is profitable.
2. Brake the wheels. Steadiness brings good luck.
1. Getting his tail wet brings regret.

Tai Chi Chuan

Nei Ching, the Yellow Emperor's Book of Internal Medicine (third–second millenium B.C.) mentioned breathing exercises of the extremities. This was the beginning of Tai Chi Chuan. "Chi," the emanations of heaven and earth, has been mentioned in Chinese classics ever since, and included the I Ching (ninth–eighth century B.C.).

As early as 190 A.D., Hau T'o, founder of Chinese surgery, wrote about a system of exercises called the frolics of the five animals, the tiger, deer, bear, monkey, and bird. Using deep breathing methods, he invented a form of circular movements intended to bring man to his full potential and normal longevity of one hundred years. The exercise proceeded by directing the breath into the upper, middle and lower abdomen through deliberate concentration of the mind and the banishing of all wandering thoughts, thus achieving a spiritual void.

In about 535 A.D., Budhidharma, founder of Zen Buddhism and abbot of the Shaoling monastery in Hunan Province taught the monks a boxing technique of breathing and sensomotoric control in eighteen movements, named Shao-ling, for relaxation and self-defense. Around 960 A.D., Chang-Sanfeng, a Taoist priest of Mt. Wutang Hupeh Province, taught the soft and internal form of boxing with the emphasis on breathing. But the form of movement as we know it today came from a General Chen Wong-ding of Hunan Province at the end of the Ming Dynasty (early seventeenth century), the emhasis being more on self-defense than on meditation. After the Opium War (1842), the sound of British guns awakened us to the futility of the technique of Chuan (fist, or boxing) on the battlefield. The emphasis was then shifted to health, the harmony of body and mind. There are four main styles of Tai Chi Chuan today: Yang (long and slow), Wu (short and slow), Vu (shorter and slower), and Sun (long and fast). The sequence presented in this book is currently practiced on mainland China, officially published by the Peking government in January of 1961. It combines all of the four styles.

The Basic Principles

1. Harmony

Move your feet, knees, legs, waist, hand, and head in a harmonious sequence; they are like the pearls in a string, well-balanced, changing from Yin to Yang, insubstantial to substantial, space to form, full to empty, flowing like a river.

2. Circular Movement

Move in circles and curves, all sizes in many directions, horizontal, vertical, or slanted, opposite or concurrent—the circle of containment and detachment, the movement being long and supple, in a rhythmic pattern.

3. Circulation of "Chi"

Breathe the essence of life, the vital energy, "Chi." Breathing starts with the mind, and engenders the movement. Make the "Chi" go into the tips of your fingers and the tips of your toes, and circulate from the top of your head to the bottoms of your feet. Breathe evenly and deeply. Store and nurture the "Chi."

4. Effortless Effort

Move as slowly as possible, as lightly as possible, as if drawing on silk. Be tranquil like a mountain. Be alert like a cat watching a mouse. Be natural like a hawk catching a rabbit. Most of all, be aware of the flow within and without.

5. Looseness

Loosen your shoulders and drop your elbows so your "Chi" sinks into your lower belly (t an-t'ien). Contain your chest, flex your back, relax your loins, and stay rooted on your feet like a tree is rooted to the earth. The breath is the wheel, the waist is the axletree.

BASIC STEPS

The body is naturally erect, feet apart as wide as shoulders, parallel to each other, with toes pointing straight ahead. The center of gravity is between the two feet. Both hands drop naturally to the sides. Eyes look straight ahead. The whole body is loose and breathing naturally.

Empty Step

Take a step forward. The weight is on the back foot; the front foot is slightly touching the ground. The knees are slightly bent.

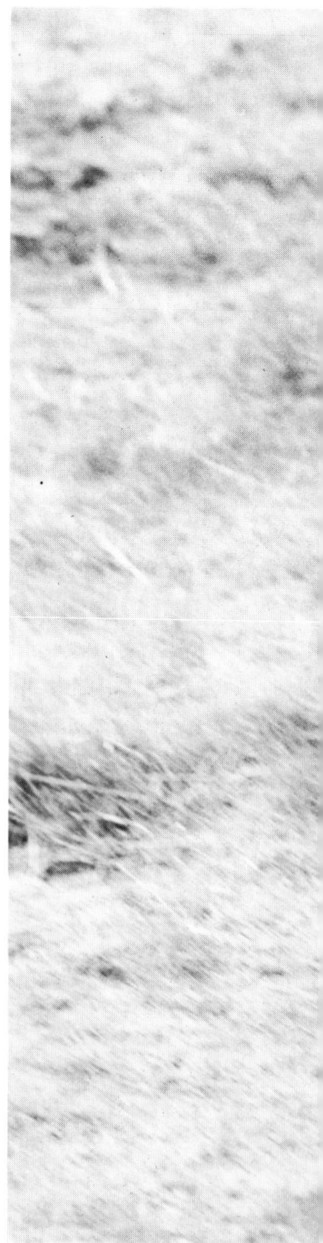

Arrow Step

Take a step forward. The weight is on the front foot, front knee is bent (but not over the toes). Toes are pointing straight ahead. Back foot is slightly touching the ground. The toes slant slightly outward to the side.

Sweeping Step

Take a step to the side, as wide as possible. One knee is bent, the other straight (but the bent knee does not extend over the toes). The feet are fully on the ground with the toes slightly slanting to the sides.

Ball-holding Position

Take a step to the side. The weight is on one foot. One hand is raised to the armpit, palm down. The other hand circles down to the waist, palm up. The hands curve naturally to fit the top and bottom of a ball.
Elbows dropping at sides
Fingers slightly bent
Buttocks tucked in
ESSENCE: Shoulders sink, elbows drop, fingers curve naturally. Gravity is in the middle of the two feet. Bend knees and waist loose, buttocks pulled in. The dropping of both arms is harmonious with the bending of the knees.

1. Opening Position Hands

A. Stand erect
naturally
Feet parallel at
shoulders' width
Eyes looking
straight ahead
Neck straight
Chin slightly in
Shoulders loose
Tongue touching
palate

B. Two arms slowly
lifting until reaching
shoulders' height
Palms facing down

C. Upper torso erect
Knees slightly bent
Palms simultaneously
pushing down

2. Wild Horse Ruffling Mane

A. Body slightly turning right
Weight shift to right foot
Left foot moving toward the right foot
Meantime right hand withdrawing toward chest
Eyes looking at right hand
B. Upper body turning left
Right foot pivoting inward
Left foot stepping out to the left forming an arrow step
Meantime left hand raises to eye level and right hand pushes down to right hip
Eyes looking at left hand

C. Shifting weight to right foot as body sits back
Left toes lift up and pivot outward
Body turning left
Weight shifting to left foot forming an arrow step
Meantime left hand withdrawing toward chest
Right hand moving under left hand simulating "ball-holding"
Right foot moving toward left foot

Right heel up, tiptoes
Eyes looking at left hand
D. Right foot stepping forward, forming arrow step
Meantime left and right hand separating, right hand up and left hand down
Right hand at eye level (palm slanting upward)
Left hand at side of left hip (palm facing down)
Eyes looking at right hand
E. The same as C, but left and right are opposite
F. The same as D, but left and right are opposite

ESSENCE: Upper body remains erect. The chest is expanding, but comfortably. The separating of the two hands is in a circular manner. The waist is the axle when pivoting. The speed of stepping out and separating hand should be even and harmonious.

3. White Crane Flapping Wings

A. Body slightly turning left
Right hand turning over moving toward left, simulating "ball-holding"
B. Right foot moves foward half a step
Body sitting back
Weight shifting to right foot
Left foot slightly moving forward on tiptoe
Meantime right hand moving up and left hand moving down
Right hand resting

near the right forehead (palm facing in)
Left hand at the side of the left hip (palm facing down)
Eyes looking ahead
ESSENCE: Avoid stiffening chest. The ups and downs of the two arms should maintain a semicircle. The left knee is slightly bent.

4. Brush Knee Twist Step

A. Right hand moving downward and circling back and up (palm facing upward)
Left hand circling up resting in front of right chest
Meantime body turning right
Eyes looking at right hand
B. Body turning left
Left foot stepping forward forming arrow step
Right hand passing by the side of the ear and pushing forward at the level of the tip of the nose
Left hand sweeping down brushes left knee
Eyes looking at right forefinger

C. Right leg slowly bends
Body sitting back
Weight shifting to the right
Left toes left up, slightly pivoting outward
Weight shifting to the left forming arrow step
Body turning left
Right foot moving toward left foot on tiptoe
Meantime left hand turning palm and circling back and up (palm facing up)

Right hand circling up, resting in front of left shoulder (palm facing down)
Eyes looking at left hand
D. The same as B, but left and right opposite
E. The same as C, but left and right are opposite
F. The same as B

ESSENCE: The upper body remains erect while pushing out hand. Waist and pelvis loose. While pushing out hand, the shoulders sink and elbows drop. The pushing of the hand is in harmonious coordination with the waist and leg movements.

5. Hands Plucking Pipa (Lute)

A. Right foot moves toward left heel
B. Left foot moves forward half a step, forming Empty Step. Heel down, knee bent
Meantime left hand lifting up as high as the tip of the nose
Elbow bent
Right hand withdraws to the side of the left elbow
Eyes looking at left forefinger
ESSENCE: Upper body naturally well-balanced. Hips

tucked in. Sink shoulders and drop elbows; loosen chest. The raising of the left hand should be in circular manner.

6.
Step Back and Repulse Monkey

A. Right hand turning up, crossing in front of belly, circling back and up
Left hand turns up
Eyes looking at left hand
B. Right hand passing by the side of the right ear, and pushing forward (palm facing out)
Left hand withdrawing, passing across belly, back and up
Meantime, left foot slightly lifting and back one step, forming an Empty Step
Eyes looking at right hand
C. The same as B, but left and right are opposite
D. Same as B
note: when stepping back, toes first eyes follow moving hand
ESSENCE: When pushing hand out, the arm must be slightly bent. While withdrawing, the hand must travel in a

circular path. Avoid stiffness; when stepping back, the toes touch first. When stepping back with the left foot, slant foot slightly to the left; when stepping back with the right foot, slant to the right slightly. In empty step, the front knee is slightly bent. While stepping back, the body is well-balanced and stable. The eyes follow the turning of the body to the left and to the right and then look at the front hand.

7. Left Hand Grasping Sparrow's Tail

A. Body turning right
Left hand circling down and up to the right side of the waist
Right hand bending in to the chest, simulating "ball-holding"
Meantime, right toes pivoting outward
Left foot moves toward right foot on tiptoe
B. Left foot stepping out
Right toes pivoting slightly inward
Weight on left, forming arrow step
Meantime, left arm coming up to the shoulder level, with elbow bending naturally
Right hand dropping down to the right side of the hip (palm facing down)
Eyes looking at left forearm
C. Left hand turns, palm facing down
Right hand turning, palm facing up, moving up, resting below left wrist
Both hands circling downward, passing in front of the belly and back, until right hand is as high as the shoulder, palm facing up, and left hand is resting in front of the chest, palm facing in
Meantime, weight shifting to the right foot
Eyes looking at right hand
D. Right hand coming in toward chest
Both hands continue out to the left, right hand as if pushing left wrist (left palm

facing in, right palm
facing out)
Meantime, weight
shifting left, forming
arrow step
Eyes looking at
left wrist
E. Turning both hands
palms downward
Body sitting back
Left toes lift up, weight
shifts to right foot
Both hands withdraw
to front of the chest,
palms slanting down
Eyes looking straight
ahead

F. Both hands pushing out until reaching shoulder height Meantime, weight shifts to the left foot, forming arrow step Eyes looking straight ahead
ESSENCE: While pushing out, both arms move in a circular manner. The separating ward off:
(a) of the hands, the loosening of the waist and the bending of the leg should be coordinated and harmonious.
roll back:
(b) Upper body erect; hips tucked in. The rolling back of the arms should follow the pivoting of the waist in a circular fashion. The weight is on the back foot.
press:
(c) Upper body erect; the back is not bent. The pressing of the arm to the front should be in harmonious coordination with the loosening of the waist and bending of the leg.
push:
(d) The arms are pushing ahead from the waist and pelvis. The shoulders sink and the elbows drop. The wrists are at shoulder level. Loosen both the pelvis and the waist.

8. Right Hand Grasping Sparrow's Tail

A. Upper body sitting back, turning right
Weight shifted to right foot
Left toes pivoting in
Right hand moves out to the right and circles down to the left, passing in front of the belly, palms facing up
Left hand resting in front of the chest, simulating a "ball-holding" with the right hand
Meantime, weight shifting to the left foot
Right foot moves in toward left foot on tiptoe

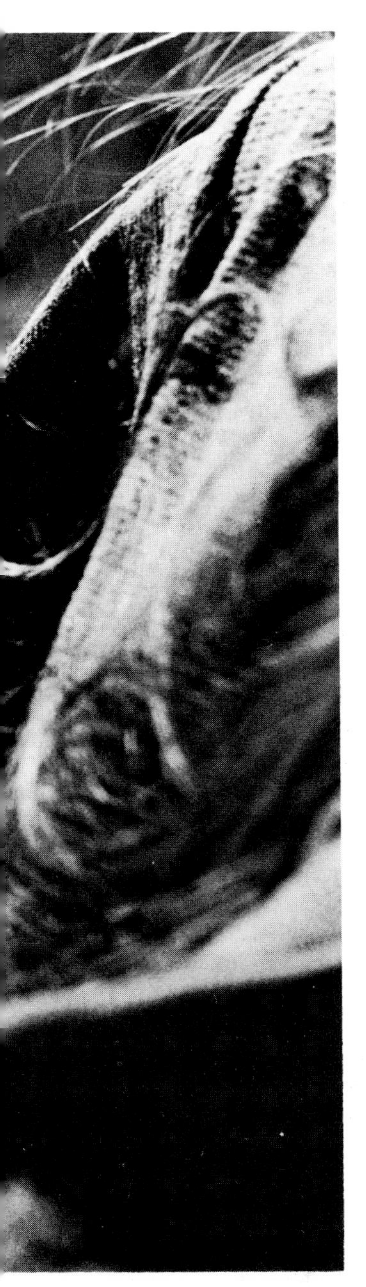

B. The same as B, of Left Hand Grasping Sparrow's Tail, but left and right are opposite
C. The same as C, of Left Hand Grasping Sparrow's Tail, but left and right are opposite
D. The same as D, of Left Hand Grasping Sparrow's Tail, but left and right are opposite
E. The same as E, of Left Hand Grasping Sparrow's Tail, but left and right are opposite
F. The same as F, of Left Hand Grasping Sparrow's Tail, but left and right are opposite
ESSENCE: Same as Left Hand Grasping Sparrow's Tail

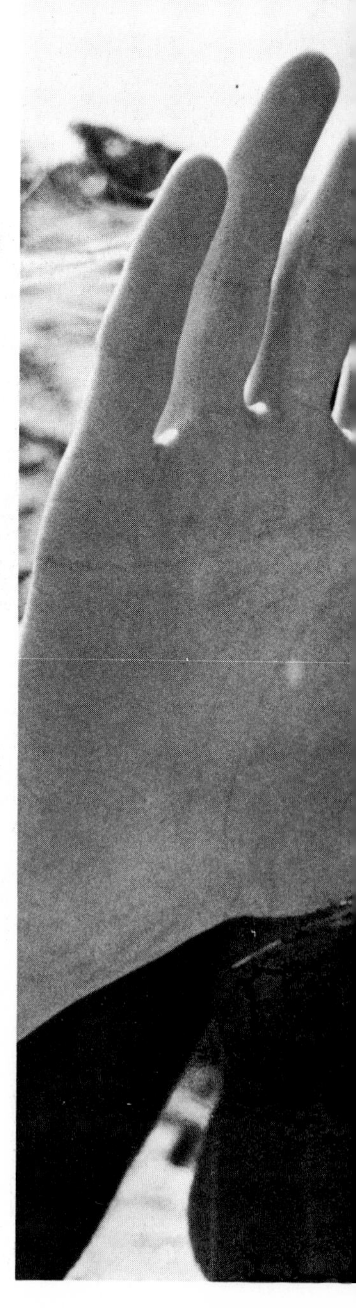

9. Single Whip

A. Upper body sitting back
Weight gradually shifting to left foot
Right toes pivoting in
Meantime upper body turning left
Both hands (left high, right low) passing by front of the chest moving to the left until the left arm points left, horizontally and right arm rests in front of left chest, horizontally
Eyes looking at left hand
B. Weight slowly shifting to right foot
Left foot moves toward right foot
Meantime, right hand moves upward to the right, forming a hook with the fingers
Left hand circles down and up, resting in front of right shoulder (palm facing in)
Eyes looking at left hand
C. Upper body turning left slightly
Left foot stepping out, forming left arrow step
Meantime, left palm turns and pushes left, palm facing out, fingers on eye level
Both elbows slightly bent
Eyes looking at left hand
ESSENCE: Upper body erect. Loosen the waist. Avoid falling forward. Right arm slightly bent. Left elbow matches the left knee. Shoulders sink. The whole body moves harmoniously.

10. Cloud

A. Weight shifting to right foot
Body slowly turning right
Left toes pivoting in
Left hand circling up, passing in front of the right shoulder, palms slanting in
Right "hook" becomes flat hand, palm facing up
Eyes looking at left hand
B. Weight slowly shifting to the left
Left hand passing in front of the face and continues out to the left
Right hand circling left, passing in front of the belly and resting in front of the left shoulder, palm slanting in
Meantime, right foot moving toward the left foot, stopping at shoulders' width
Eyes looking at right hand
C. Right hand stretches to the right
Left hand circling right, passing in front of the belly, resting in front of the right shoulder, palm slanting in
Meantime, right hand turns palm, facing out
Left foot stepping out to the left
Eyes looking at left hand
D. The same as B
E. The same as C
F. The same as B
ESSENCE: The pivoting of the body should hinge on the waist and the spine. Avoid ups and downs

of the posture. Loosen waist and pelvis. The arms follow the pivoting of the waist. Be alive and natural. While shifting weight from one foot to the other, the gravity should be stabilized. Eyes follow the moving of the left and right hands.

11. Single Whip

middle of the two hands
C. Both arms separate horizontally (palms facing out)
Meantime, right foot slowly lifting and kicking out sideways
Eyes looking at right hand
ESSENCE: Body is stable; avoid bending forward or backward. When separating hands, the wrists are on the shoulder level. The left knee is slightly bent. When kicking up, the toes curl up. The separating of the hand and kicking of the foot should be in harmonious coordination. Right arm and right leg match each other.

14. Twin Peaks Piercing Ears

A. Right foot pulls up
Both hands simultaneously circling down, resting at two sides of the right knee, palms facing up
B. Right foot stepping out to form right arrow step
Meantime, both hands dropping down to hips forming fists
Fists circle back, then out to the front, eyes of the fists facing each other and slightly apart

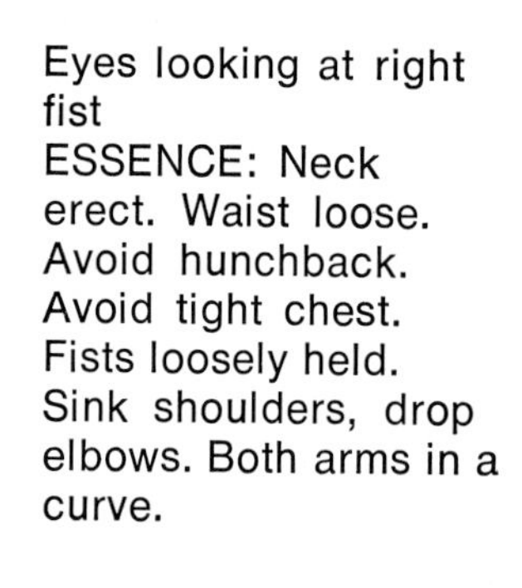
Eyes looking at right fist
ESSENCE: Neck erect. Waist loose. Avoid hunchback. Avoid tight chest. Fists loosely held. Sink shoulders, drop elbows. Both arms in a curve.

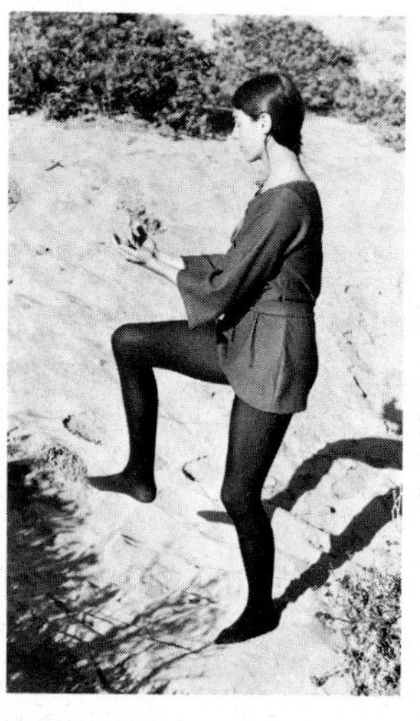

15. Turn Body Left Frog Kick

A. Weight gradually shifting to the left
Right toes pivoting in (as body turns left)
Meantime, both fists becoming flat hands
Hands separating and circling down, palms facing out
Eyes looking at left hand
B. Weight shifting to the right
Left foot moving toward the right foot
Meantime, both hands circling up, crossing in front of the chest, left hand on the outside, both palms facing in
Eyes looking at the middle of the two hands
C. Hands separating horizontally, both palms facing out
Meantime, left foot lifting up and slowly kicking out sideways
Eyes looking at left hand
ESSENCE: Same as Right Frog Kick, but left and right are opposite.

16. Left Creeping Snake (and Golden Rooster Standing on One Leg)

A. Left foot pulls in, while right hand becomes hook
Left hand circling to the right, resting vertical at right shoulder
Eyes looking at left hand
B. Body slowly squatting
Left foot steps sideways to the left, forming "sweeping step"
Left hand circling down, then up to the left

Eyes looking at left hand
note: right toes slightly pivoting out, left toes pivoting in, both feet fully on the ground
C. Body rising, weight shift to the left foot
Right leg slowly straightening up
Left toes pivoting out, right toes pivoting in

Meantime, left arm stretching to the front, palm standing vertically
Eyes looking at left hand
D. Right leg slowly lifting up
Meantime, right hook becoming flat hand, circling front and up
Right hand bends elbow, palm vertical with elbow just above right knee
Left hand dropping to the side of the left hip, palm facing down

Eyes looking at right hand
note: left leg slightly bent
ESSENCE: (A) Right leg completely squatting, right toe slanting out; left leg stretched straight, left toes slanting in. Both feet fully on the ground. Upper body avoid bending over too much.
(B) Standing leg bends slightly. Upper body erect. Be still.

17. Right Creeping Snake (and Golden Rooster Standing on One Leg)

A. Right foot dropping in front of the left foot on tiptoe
Body turning left, left heel pivoting in
Meantime, left hand circling back and up, forming a hook
Right hand circling to the left, resting vertical at left shoulder
Eyes looking at right hand
B. The same as B of Left Creeping Snake, but left and right are opposite
C. The same as C of Left Creeping Snake, but left and right are opposite
D. The same as D of Left Creeping Snake, but left and right are opposite
ESSENCE: (A) Same as Left Creeping Snake A., but left and right opposite. (B) Same as Left Creeping Snake B., but left and right are opposite.

18. Jade Maiden Threading Shuttle

A. Body slightly turning left
Left foot drops down, toes pivoting out
Right heel up, and pivot
Both hands simulating a "ball-holding" position (left hand above, right hand below)
Right foot moves toward the left foot on tiptoe
Eyes looking at left forearm
B. Right foot stepping forward, forming

arrow step
Meantime, right hand comes up in front of the face, resting at right side of the forehead, palm slanting up
Left hand pushing out in front of the chest, palm facing forward
Eyes looking at left hand

C. Weight shifting back
Right toe slightly pivoting out
Left foot moves toward right foot, resting on tiptoe
Meantime, both hands simulating "ball-holding" (right up, left down)
Eyes looking at right forearm
D. The same as B, but left and right opposite
ESSENCE: Upper body erect. When raising hand, avoid raising shoulder. When pushing forward, the waist and the leg move in harmonious coordination.

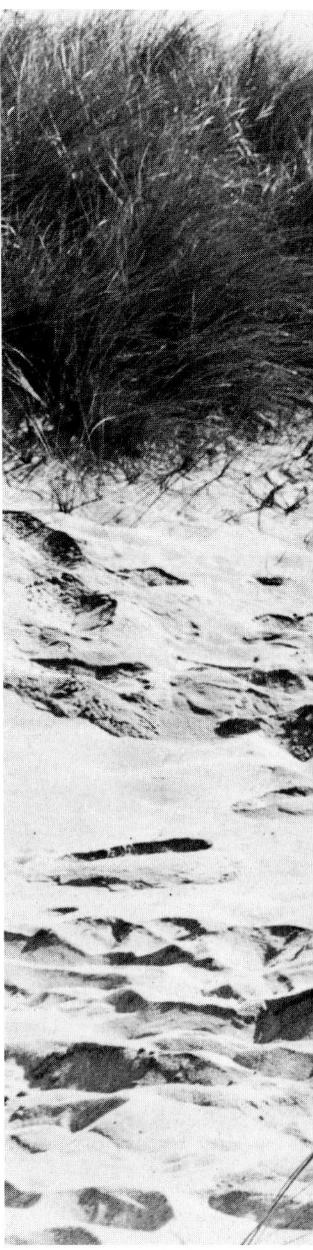

19. Needle at the Bottom of the Sea

A. Right foot moves to the left foot
Left foot slightly stepping forward on tiptoe, forming left "empty step"
Meantime, right hand rises in front of the body to the side of the right ear
Left hand drops to the side of the left hip
Eyes looking straight ahead

ESSENCE: Body slightly bent. Neck erect. Hips tucked in. When plunging right hand, keep shoulder in position. Left knee slightly bent.

20. Fanning Out Arms

A. Upper body slightly turning right
Left foot stepping out, forming left arrow step
Right hand rises from the front up toward the right side of the forehead, palm slanting out
Meantime, left hand passes in front of the chest, then pushes out ahead, palm facing the front
Eyes looking at left hand
note: the left hand is as high as the tip of the nose
ESSENCE: Upper body erect naturally. Loosen waist and hip. Do not stretch left arm straight. Expand the back muscles. Left hand is as high as the tip of the nose.

21.
Turn Body, Deflect, Parry and Punch

A. Right leg bending, weight shifts to right foot
Left toes pivot in
Body turning right, weight shifting to the left
Meantime, right hand circling down (forming fist), passing in front of the belly, and stops in front of the left chest (facing down)
Left hand lifts up, stopping in front of the forehead, palm slanting up
Eyes looking straight ahead
B. Body turning right
Right fist passing across front of chest, thrusts out, fists facing up and elbow bending
Left hand drops to the side of the left hip
Meantime, right foot swings back and steps out to the front, toes pivoting out
Eyes looking at right fist
C. Weight shifts to right foot
Left foot steps forward
Left hand circling to the front and pushing out
Right fist comes back to the side of the waist, fist facing up
Eyes looking at left hand

D. Left foot steps to the front, forming arrow step
Meantime, right fist thrusting out ahead
Left hand meets right forearm
Eyes looking at right fist
note: right fist loosely held and right arm slightly bending
ESSENCE: Right fist loosely held; right shoulder follows the movement of the right fist. Sink shoulders, drop elbows. Avoid stretching right arm straight.

22.
As Is Closing Door

A. Left hand thrusting out below the right wrist
Right fist becoming flat hand
Both palms facing up, slowly withdrawing
Meantime, weight shifting to right foot
Left toes left up
Eyes looking straight ahead
B. Both hands turn outward at the chest, then push out, palms facing forward
Meantime, forming left arrow step

Eyes looking at the middle of the two palms

ESSENCE: While sitting back, avoid swaying backwards. Buttocks tucked in. While the two hands withdraw, the elbows and shoulders expand slightly out to the sides.

23. Crossing Hands

A. Weight shifting to the right
Left toes pivot in, body turning right
Right hand stretching to the right horizontally as the left stretches to the left horizontally, elbows slightly bent
Meantime, left toes pivoting out, forming a right arrow step
Eyes looking at right hand
B. Weight slowly shifting to the left foot
Right foot moves to the left, forming "opening step"
Meantime both hands circling down, passing in front of the belly and up, crossing in front of the chest, right hand on the outside (palms facing in)
Eyes looking straight ahead
ESSENCE: Body standing up naturally. Chin tucked in slightly. Arms maintain a semicircle in front of the chest. Sink shoulders, drop elbows, whole body is fully relaxed and comfortable.

24. Closing Position

A. Hands turning downward, palms facing down, separating and resting at sides of the hips Eyes looking straight ahead

ESSENCE: Both hands separating to the left and right and drop downward. Whole body is loose. Eyes looking straight forward.

TAI CHI
A WAY OF CENTERING
AND
I CHING

A Book of Oracle
Imagery, in a new
translation

by Gia-fu Feng
and Jerome Kirk
Photographs by
Hugh L. Wilkerson
With Forewords by
Alan W. Watts and
Laura Huxley

COLLIER BOOKS
COLLIER-MACMILLAN LTD., LONDON

Designed by William Hopkins and Ira Friedlander

Library of Congress Catalog Card Number: 70-97757

First Collier Books Edition 1970

This book is also published in a hardcover edition by
The Macmillan Company

The Macmillan Company
866 Third Avenue, New York, N. Y. 10022
Collier-Macmillan Canada Ltd., Toronto, Ontario

Printed in the United States of America